DARK FIRE

✲ ✲ ✲ ✲ ✲ ✲ ✲ ✲ ✲ ✲ ✲

Dark Fire

* * * * * * * * * * * *

Bernadette Rule

IRONING BOARD PRESS

ISBN 978-1-7776440-0-0

bernadetterule.ca

For
Ernest & Ola Lawrence & their children:
Fred, Ethelyn & Ralph
Ottus & Lora Drew & their children:
Harry, Adell & Madine
& for Delmer Drew

May they rest in peace

*There were not found women fair as the Daughters of Job
in all the Land & their Father gave them inheritance among
    their Brethren.
If I ascend up into Heaven Thou are there.
If I make my bed in Hell behold Thou art there.*

—William Blake *"Job & His Daughters"* engraving, 1825

Prologue

IT'S 1962 AND I'M IN THE SEVENTH GRADE at St. Joseph's School in Greenberry, Kentucky. A woman dressed in the medieval widow's garb which is the Ursuline habit stands in front of a bulletin board that reads, in letters a foot high: *IT IS A HOLY AND WHOLESOME THOUGHT TO PRAY FOR THE DEAD*. She is telling me and the fifty other children in the room that Kentucky is an Iroquoian word meaning dark and bloody battleground.

Sister Clarentia has an expressive face imprisoned in her stiff wimple, and her dark eyes and white teeth flash as she delivers this rather toxic phrase. My friends and I grimace at each other. Why couldn't Kentucky mean something pretty like where the rippling waters flow? Why on earth did it have to be called Dark and Bloody Battleground?

I look through the second storey windows to the quiet streetscape—the housetops of blue or green tiles, birds singing from every wire and branch. It seems perfectly peaceful to me. Our town of 6,000 people is arranged around the red-brick courthouse a few blocks to the east of the school. Its spire pierces the sky at the center of a leafy court square. A neat block of stores faces the courthouse on all four sides, with tree-lined residential streets beyond. Nothing dark and bloody about it as far as I can see.

Because of this very Kentucky History class I know that Greenberry is the county seat and geographic heart of Wills County, the county itself a perfect rectangle in the southwestern corner of the state, eighteen miles across and thirty miles long. It produces ball clay, soybeans, corn, cattle and a little oil and gas. But mostly it produces dark fired tobacco.

Though my family lives in town, we have friends and relatives on farms scattered all around the county, so I've seen a good deal of this land that's supposed to be so blood-soaked. I've skirted herds of chewing cows, climbed fences and jumped creeks, feasted on wild berries, sour grass and honeysuckle blossoms. I've slapped at mosquitoes under wide shade trees, and inhaled the rich aroma of freshly turned earth. These fields seem to me to stretch away forever in all directions, with only throngs of insects to groan over them.

Once some friends and I came across a slit pig in a creek-bed, grey and purple innards spilling out of it. That was bloody alright, but this phrase troubling me now hints more at treachery between humans, than between people and animals. Sister has told us how Daniel Boone and Simon Kenton drove out the Indians. So, did the Indians only name the land as they were leaving it? Or were the battles they named it for ancient wars between Indian tribes, fought before Boone and Kenton ever arrived? How far back does the darkness go?

The recess bell rings and, jarred back to the orderly classroom, I close my Kentucky History book and stow it in the cubbyhole under my seat. The others are way ahead of me, filing carefully past Sister and into the hall to surge, just under a run, towards the playground.

*　*　*　*　*　*　*　*　*　*　*

Sometimes Daddy takes us out to the cemetery to visit family graves. Today, instead of going to St. Joseph's country graveyard where most of our people are buried, he's taking me and three of my brothers and sisters to Maplewood, the big cemetery in town. His father, Hardin Rule, is buried there because Hardin and *his* folks were Methodists. In 1905 my grandparents' Catholic/Protestant marriage was frowned upon, but my grandmother told me once that she married Hardin because, 'He was the handsomest man I'd ever seen, and in all the years since I've never had cause to change that opinion.'

In a reflective mood, Daddy strides among the tombstones, telling stories about people we never knew. Patiently, he allows us to wander around, commenting on inscriptions and asking questions. Then, as if struck with sudden inspiration, he says, Y'all come over here. I want to show you something.

Daddy was often a distant figure to me, full of mystery and authority. He was usually evasive, tantalizingly beyond my reach. (Where you going, Daddy? Going to see a man about a dog. Can I go? No.) So to have him invite us into a secret is a moment of thrilling privilege. I scamper behind him as he threads the family plots of Maplewood, lambs and angels tumbling in my peripheral vision.

He stops in front of a plainish white stone, slightly larger than average, and when we all catch up he reads its inscription out loud:

> *In memory of the Lawrence and Drew families,*
> *Eleven in number, who met a horrible death*
> *in the burning of the Lawrence home near*
> *Hickory, Kentucky on the night of June 25, 1921*
> *One of the unsolved mysteries*

After Daddy finishes reading it, the words of the epitaph seem to echo from stone to stone in the quiet cemetery. They are chilling, especially the phrases *horrible death in the burning*, and *unsolved mysteries*. I don't understand, but I can tell that Daddy is poised to explain. He stands before the tombstone with his feet spaced far apart, gives a sigh, and begins.

This right here is what's called a mass grave. There's eleven people buried in it: two young couples with three little babies apiece, and a twelve-year-old boy named Delmer. They were my first cousins.

As the surprise of our close relationship to this gruesome business settles into us, we begin firing questions at him. Eventually he answers them all, saying once or twice, Now this is important. You re*member* what I'm telling you.

Why were they buried all together?

Cause, they were so burnt up there wasn't enough left of em to fill but one casket.

How'd their house catch on fire?

Now then, Daddy says, pointing his long finger at my brother Michael. *Now* then. You've done hit on the main question. You see, they didn't die in a house fire like it says here. These people were murdered, and the house *set* on fire to cover up the evidence.

*Murd*ered…

How?

Who did it?

Why would anybody wanna murder em?

You mean the boy and the little babies too?

Whoa, wait a minute, he says, pleased at our interest, but wishing to take the story more slowly. All of you take a good long look at that tombstone and when you've got it fixed in your mind, follow me on back to the car. I'll tell you the whole story—*if*, he says, wheeling around to look at us again, you promise me you won't ever forget it. Cause this is one of the most important stories I'm ever liable to tell you.

✳ ✳ ✳ ✳ ✳ ✳ ✳ ✳ ✳ ✳ ✳

Daddy told us only part of the story that day. He told us that the Lawrence's log cabin, the one that got burned down, was the same house his father, Hardin, had been born and raised in. When Hardin's father died his mother sold the farm to the Oakley family and moved into town. One of the Oakley daughters married a Lawrence and another one married a Drew. They were the two women who—along with their husbands and children, and twelve-year-old Delmer—were killed that night.

People said some of the other Oakleys were jealous that their *sisters* had gotten the home-place, and they—the jealous ones— joined in with a group of men called Night Riders to ambush the

Drews and Lawrences while the two families were having a Saturday night singalong party. The Night Riders rode around and around the house, firing in through the windows and then set the place on fire.

Daddy, fourteen at the time, was awakened in the dead of night by a man riding into town like Paul Revere to announce the news to the relatives. After hearing about the fire Daddy'd gone out to the scene with his parents and aunts and uncles, and he'd seen the house burning with the bodies still scattered around inside.

My papa climbed a big tree beside the house and he come back down white as a sheet, shaking his head and saying, They're all in there. He said most of em was laying in the floor, shot, but one of the young mothers was laying across a bed trying to shield her three babies, like this. Here Daddy reached out to embrace the air in an attitude of tender grief. But they were all of em already dead when we got there. And we couldn't get to em to pull em out. Just had to stand there and watch em burn up. We like to've never got over that night—and Aunt Ruth, she never did.

The night Daddy told us the story, I lay awake in the room I shared with my sister and two brothers, afflicted with grotesque images. Sorrow, especially for the mother and her babies, swelled and ached inside my chest. The term Night Riders held me rigid with fear. Daddy's assurances that there weren't any Night Riders anymore had been only slightly helpful, for they had already become boogie men in my imagination, and I knew boogie men could get *any*body.

✻ ✻ ✻ ✻ ✻ ✻ ✻ ✻ ✻ ✻ ✻

It wasn't until I grew up that I learned Night Riders were real, and that they did get people. Strangely enough, Night Riding began as part of a desperate and even noble move to secure a decent living for tobacco farmers.

By the end of the nineteenth century factory-rolled cigarettes were the new sensation, and had made Buck Duke his fortune down in North Carolina. His company, American Tobacco, had bought up virtually all of its worldwide competition, and had a stranglehold on the market. They became the only game in town for farmers looking to sell their crop.

In 1904 the American Tobacco Company was offering farmers three cents a bushel—four cents less than they had gotten a few years before, and even less than it cost to *plant* the crop. After several years of chronic poverty, Felix Ewing—The Moses of the Black Patch—began working to form a planters' union. By pooling our crops and holding them off the market, he said, we can force the big companies to pay us more. But only if we *all* work together.

At first the method was successful. Duke was astonished that a bunch of farmers—independent cusses as they'd always been—could work together to influence the market. So he began offering ten cents a bushel to anyone who would break with the union and sell at the barn door instead of at the chute.

This was the devil's own temptation to people who hadn't been able to pay their bills or buy their children shoes for years. Some caved. That was when David Amoss entered the story and what became known as the Black Patch War began. In the field, dark fired tobacco is a much darker green than the more common, yellowish burley tobacco. Hence, the areas of western Kentucky and Tennessee that grow dark fired tobacco are called the Black Patch.

A doctor from Cobb, Kentucky, David Amoss was an avid supporter of the new union, and a romantic on the subject of the Civil War, which he always regretted narrowly missing by having been born in 1857. Amoss formed the Night Riders to be a militant branch of the union, which would bring pressure to bear on farmers who wavered, reminding them that all the little fish had to hold together against the big fish or they wouldn't stand a chance.

He went to the Ku Klux Klan to investigate their methods, one being the use of stereotypical fears poor people, especially blacks, were believed to hold about things such as ghosts and midnight. Like the Klan, Night Riders began as a tchnically non-violent vigilante movement on the part of lower class whites. And just as the Klan soon moved from emotional violence to physical violence, so did the Night Riders.

The attempt to form a union of tobacco planters began to look like the Civil War all over again—brother against brother, neighbor against neighbor. In fact, as the Civil War had ended only forty years before, the old allegiances to North and South still operated in such matters as, say, the choice of which neighborhood to live in. Western Kentucky was a checkerboard of Northern or Southern sympathizers, and each section bore its grudges dutifully. Night Riders took their mission equally seriously. Using Klan tactics, they always rode out in a body, their coats inside-out to avoid easy recognition. Feed-sacks were employed to muffle horses' hooves, and to shield the identity of horse and rider. They would approach their target at midnight, riding up to the porch of a remote farmhouse and calling the farmer's name.

At first, they did little more than call people out to give them a serious warning that they'd better not be thinking of selling their crop just yet. Eventually, if these warnings weren't heeded, they would make another visit. This time they would tie the farmer, and often his wife as well, to a tree and beat him with hickory sticks or buggy-whip him. The beatings were gradually supplemented with crop destruction and barn burnings.

Townsfolk were not spared either. After all, they ran the chute where the tobacco was sold, or the warehouses where it was stored. They preached sermons, gave or withheld credit at the stores, controlled the courts, the newspapers and the banks. They, therefore, also had to be made to understand what was at issue in this struggle, and to take the union's side.

In 1907 Hopkinsville, Kentucky was besieged by a band of Night Riders so organized they might have been putting a docile baby to bed instead of taking over a whole town. Swiftly and silently the depot and telephone office were seized; the mayor was chased right down the coal chute of the Baptist Church; the newspaper— whose editor had written articles questioning the union's aims and methods—was disabled in the smashing of its presses; and finally, the biggest tobacco warehouses were burnt to the ground while the police and fire brigades stood and watched, as they were told to. After this success, small towns all over western Kentucky and Tennessee were liable to be besieged by disgruntled Night Riders. (Greenberry's turn would come in 1920, during the second phase of the Black Patch War.)

By 1911 when Roosevelt busted the tobacco trust and assured farmers a fairer market, the few court cases against Night Riders fizzled out and the movement went into remission. Until after the First World War, that is. The war had boosted tobacco prices considerably (*Cigarettes for our boys in the trenches!*), and farmers were feeling the happy effects when, in 1920, the market suddenly plunged again. Ever watchful, Felix Ewing and other old union leaders began calling meetings and a second round of Night Riding commenced, this time with many returned soldiers in its ranks, newly graduated from the ugly academy of war.

The Drews and Lawrences were victims of *this* round of Night Riding. When, as an adult, I returned to Daddy's story and began to research it for myself, I discovered that his version, so graphic and frightening to me as a child, had been softened and amended. The truth was both more brutal, and more complex than I had imagined. I also discovered that the aftermath of World War One in Wills County, as in many other places, was a period of history marked by violent change and by so much grey it is almost impossible to define the good guys and the bad guys.

One thing is clear to me. The Drews and Lawrences paid some sort of community debt with their blood. After their murders, Night Riding tapered off dramatically, and had ceased altogether by about 1930, when the union that is still in place today was established. Perhaps the men involved were shocked sober by the evil of which they had found themselves capable. As far as I have been able to determine, the massacre of the Drews and Lawrences marked the bloodiest and last large scale action by Night Riders, though it should be noted that the terrorizing of black families by gangs using the Night Rider modus operandi continued for two or three decades. Such raids were usually confined to heckling from cars and firing bullets through the upper panes of windows. The families of men who had fought for the North during the Civil War were particularly targeted for these raids.

As with a surprising number of other crimes, no one was ever tried for the murders of the Drews and Lawrences. On the Monday following the massacre, the court was to have heard the case against a group of Night Riders indicted for burning the tobacco chute in Greenberry the year before. Instead, after a brief and cursory examination of six Drew and Lawrence neighbors, their case was sealed with a verdict of murder by persons unknown. The case against the men accused of burning the chute was continued indefinitely. The entire county, it seems, entered into an unspoken agreement not to push either matter any further. The community was silenced. In my eyes that fact—that the justice system failed the victims and their families utterly—relegates these deaths to the level of human sacrifice.

We are accustomed to thinking of human sacrifice as a primitive practice carried on in ancient jungles, not in twentieth century America. And yet Wills County, Kentucky is no more the devil's exclusive address than is the Amazon jungle. What happened to the Drews and Lawrences could and does occur periodically in human societies all over the world. That it happened in the quiet place in which I was raised astounds me.

By the time I was grown, and had learned what transpired in my own county in the 1920s, scholars were saying that Kentucky means no such thing as Dark and Bloody Battleground in any Indian language. They now say we don't know where the name comes from or what it means. But *I* now know that the old notion of how Kentucky got its name is appropriate to at least one field in my county. This is the story of that field. To remember the Drew and Lawrence families, and to try and understand how this particular community could have come to such a moment, is why I have written *Dark Fire*.

Chapter One

I COME AWAKE REAL SLOW the morning after the Night Riders burnt
the chute. I lay there in my bed for what seemed like a long time, and
couldn't figure out for the life of me whether all that stuff that'd happened in the middle of the night was real, or something I had dreamed.
The sun was streamin in the front window, and as my mind caught
up to me I realized it was jist ordinary sunlight. It didn't shift around
none. I could tell by the kind of silence in the house, that Mama and
Papa had already left for the Woolen Mills. At that time Bernard, who
was thirteen, worked Saturdays at Uncle Berry's grocery store. His
bed was empty. The only ones at home was me and Bridget Ruth. She
was three years older'n me so that'd put her at about eleven years old
then. It was March 26, 1920 when the Night Riders took over the town
and burnt down the tobacco chute. And living on 13th Street right
across from it, we seen it all. But I'm gettin ahead of my story.

So I was a-layin there in my bed, and looked over and seen that
Bridget Ruth was still sleepin. She had thick shiny black hair and I
can see it yet, spread out over her pillow. I got up real quiet-like and
went over to the window. The shade was nearly all the way down,
and the sunlight was jist apourin in around it. I didn't raise it—shoot
no—I didn't want nobody to see me there. I was still scared from the
night before so I jist peeped out at the edge.

But when I looked out that east window the sun was like a torch thrust right into my face. My eyes watered and I squinted up good, and by and by I seen that the view was completely altered. The chute was gone and there was men all around what was left of it.

You see our neighborhood was called Boxtown, on account of the little, wooden, boxy houses scattered around them big old tobacco warehouses. It was the part of Greenberry where the tobacco market was. And it was mixed, but mostly colored. We was one of the few white families livin there. We lived there because Granny Rule, Papa's mama, lived next door. *She'd* moved into town after her husband died and she sold the farm and give up raisin tobacco. She chose to settle in Boxtown because it was the part of town where she felt most comfortable, havin brung her tobacco there to sell all them years.

The chute was where the farmers brought it *to*. It was a long wooden barn with a driveway right through the middle, and raised platforms on either side. The buyers from the big companies'd stand on them platforms and look down into the wagon beds with hands of tobacco piled up in em, and they'd place their bids. They come from all over the world, Holland, Spain—ever'where I reckon. I used to go over and hang around sometimes on a market day jist to listen to them accents all mixed in with the auctioneer's chant. It was mesmerizin, now that's the truth. Like music.

Then the auctioneer'd give a signal, and some guy'd pull on the rope and ring the bell and it'd be the next feller's turn. Them wagons'd be lined up all the way down 13th Street. The market's held at the coldest time of the year—December to March. Them farmers would be all bunched up in their blankets, then the bell'd give a clang, and they'd inch forward one wagon-length. It was a hard life they had.

Anyway, I was lookin out, and I seen the bell still perched on its pole, with them charred chute timbers a-stickin up behind it, and men walkin all around it—town men in suits, talkin and takin notes, reporters from the paper, and I don't know who all. Right in the middle of the street a photographer had set up his camera on a tripod stand, and jist as I was peepin out he turned around sudden-like and looked in my direction.

Well, I dropped that shade right quick and scampered into the kitchen. It was at the back of the house, and as far away from him as I could get. I didn't want no truck with them men, sure enough.

Mama'd left us some bread and butter and the milk pitcher out on the table for breakfast. And *that* mornin, I remember it as clear as yesterday, there was a jar of Granny Rule's plum preserves. So I set down and et, and thought over what had took place in the middle of the night.

We'd gone to bed that Friday night expectin jist to sleep, the way you do. But when we was all fast asleep Papa come into the front room where us kids was and rolled me out of bed, blanket and all, onto the straw matting that covered the floor. He was all in a hurry and said in a loud whisper, *Bernard! Bridget Ruth!* Y'all git down on the floor and lay still. They're carryin guns, and if they was to start shootin them bullets'd pass right *through* these walls!

Lord, I never *had* come out of sleep straight into terror that away before, though it's happened to me a time or two since. The thing was, the room was bein washed with waves of strange light that cast shadders across the walls and ceiling. And Mama was there too, a-layin on the floor, her long red hair all undone. Bridget Ruth scooted right up next to her, but I snaked over to the window.

Bernard asked Papa if it was Night Riders, and Papa said, Sure as hell is. Hundreds of em.

He'd gone to stand beside the front door. See our room was right off of the porch. My bed was between the front door and the window.

I peeped up over the sill and could see a whole slew of men millin about all over 13th Street and around the chute. They was carryin guns like Papa said, and torches too, and they had their coats turned inside-out; you could see them white labels clear as anything in the moonlight. I reckon they coulda done without all them torches, it was so bright that night. But I didn't get to see much, because as soon as ever'body seen me at the window they hissed me down again.

Then all of a sudden Papa swore. Dammit, Nell, look! Ma's out there. Good God a'mighty!

Mama got up and stood behind Papa, kindly lookin over his shoulder, and said, What in the sam hill is she doin?

I peeped over the sill again. Sure enough, there was Granny, standin out in the middle of the street in her nightclothes talkin to a bunch of men just like it was a Sunday morning and they had all jist got out of church.

Granny Rule was a tiny little woman, not much bigger'n me at the time, and I was always small for my age. Long as I knowed her she dressed all in black for her widowhood, but her nightclothes was white, and her long hair was still mostly black, even though she musta been—let me see—she must've been at least seventy-five in 1920. Anyhow, she was a sweet old woman, kindly innocent. Naive, I guess you'd say. And Papa said later that she probably just saw some of her old farmin neighbors out there and decided to go ask em what was going on. But there she was anyway, amongst a gang of Night Riders.

So Papa went out onto our porch and called to her. *Ma!* he said, still tryin to whisper at first, but finally just yellin.

When she heard his voice, she turned towards it, smilin.

Ma, git yourself over here, fore you git hurt!

Y'all scuze me a minute, she says to them men, and they watched as she walked up to our front steps. She was out of my range of vision then, but I could hear Papa tellin her it was dangerous for her to be out there in that business.

She said, Aw, Hardin, they wouldn't hurt me. They're my friends. Why, I *know* most ever one of em.

And Papa said, real frustrated-like, Dammit, Ma, that's jist the trouble!

She never would come in to our house that night, but she also didn't go back over to them men. She said she was goin over to her own porch, ' …where I can watch the excitement in peace.'

Papa muttered, I swear, I don't know how she ever lived through the Civil War.

All while Papa and Granny was talkin, I watched a man with a big coal oil can walk around the chute, pourin oil onto the frame building—for all the world like he was jist waterin his garden. He disappeared around one side of it, and come back out on the other side a minute later. When he raised his arm, some of em touched their torches to the chute down where he'd poured, and flames just *whooshed* up and run to meet each other. I give a low whistle, and Bernard, who'd crawled over behind me to have a look, he took and pulled me back down to the floor, and the whole room filled to brimmin with firelight.

* * * * * * * * * *

Right about the time I's dressed and finished my breakfast and was headin out the back door, here come Bridget Ruth a-stretchin and yawnin into the kitchen.

Where you think you're goin? she asked.

See, she was supposed to be in charge of me when Mama wasn't home. But when you're the youngest in a family, you're always catchin it from ever'body, which gits tiresome. So I said sort of snippy-like, No place.

And she said, Well you better be home here at dinnertime or Mama'll be mad at *me*. Which was true enough.

So I said I would, and headed for Delmer's.

Delmer was Aunt Ruth's boy. He would've been eleven years old in 1920. Sorry as I am to say it, that's a easy one to remember.

Aunt Ruth was Papa's oldest sister. She and her four youngest kids lived around the block from us, on the corner of 14th and North. Like Granny, Aunt Ruth'd give up on raisin tobacco when her husband died, and moved to Boxtown to be near the rest of the family. Uncle Berry—Papa and Aunt Ruth's brother—lived up on the corner of 13th, near where he run his grocery on Broadway, just the other side of the train-tracks. I guess you'd say they was clannish. Not that they didn't have lots of other friends, but in them days family stuck together.

I'd often heard Aunt Ruth say she hated livin in town. She'd moved in in 1916—I reckon I'd have been about four, though I don't remember it—but she never did git used to it. She was born and raised in the country, and it was all she had ever knowed. She kept a milk cow, a old Jersey that she called April and couldn't bear to part with, town or no town. April lived in a stable down at the end of Aunt Ruth's long yard, where her big old garden run out. Shoot, Aunt Ruth'd say—them black eyes of hers just a-flashin—I cain't even milk my cow without some dang truck comes rattlin by right up against the stable. It's a wonder she can give any milk at all.

One time when we was all visitin out at Ottus and Lora's—Aunt Ruth had give *her* farm up to her son Ottus to work—it was evenin and we was all settin outside, and the stars had begun to poke through, when a whippoorwill called out. Aunt Ruth, she'd been settin there quiet, with a grand-baby on her lap, but when that whippoorwill sounded, she set up straight, and said, *Listen*. Did y'all hear that?

I heard it, Ma, but it was jist a old whippoorwill, said Ottus.

Ain't no jist *about* a whippoorwill, Ottus. Y'all don't begin to know how much I miss that sound. To me it's the prettiest birdsong in the world.

Oh I always think it sounds too mournful to be pretty, Lora said.

Aunt Ruth jist answered, I like it. And ever'body was quiet for awhile, listenin for it to come again. Which it done, by and by.

After that I always figured Aunt Ruth was sometimes edgy because of missin the country. That day when I cut through our block to see Delmer I didn't have no thought of gettin tangled up with Aunt Ruth. I run right through her flock of Leghorn chickens that always run with Granny's Dorkings, and I scattered em to the four winds. It was March, remember, so the forsythia bushes was out, and the March flowers. It was like the whole block was bustin out in yellow.

When I run into Delmer's backyard that day, Aunt Ruth was comin up from down cellar. She was carryin a number two wash tub with her washboard in it. He ain't up yet, Pat, she said—meaning Delmer. This put a hitch in my stride, sure enough. I'll go git him while you bring me up them other two tubs, a cake of lye soap, and a ball of bluein. She set the tub on a plank she kept balanced for the purpose across two tree stumps near her big black yard kettle.

Oh boy, I was caught. I'd been itchin to tell Hollis Schultz and some of the others about last night, but I wanted to find out first what Delmer had saw. Being Aunt Ruth's laundry helper, on this mornin of all mornins, wasn't nowhere in my plan.

She come up onto the porch then, and as she passed me she says, Go on now. Didn't you hear what I said?

Yes ma'am, I answered, and probably not in the best tone neither.

I could hear her inside the house, clappin her hands together and yelling, Git on up now, younguns!

I kicked the dirt up on the path around to the cellar doors, but I arrived there all the same and had to go down them steep dark steps and do her biddin. The beam of sunlight didn't reach very far into the cellar, and the packed earth felt cold and clammy to my bare feet, but I found the washtubs and stacked em one inside the other. I reached into the cardboard box where she kept her pieces of lye soap and got me one out. Then I found her store-bought box of bluein and shook me out one little marble-sized ball. I put both of these into the top tub, and brung em up like she said. Jist as I settled em onto the plank, here come Fairy and Debry, her two youngest, out of the outhouse. We was sayin our good mornings when Aunt Ruth bawled from the pump for them to eat their breakfast and get on out there and help her with the washin.

Music to my ears, I tell you. I begun to think there was some hope of gettin away after all. Then Delmer come a-squintin out into the sunshine. He nodded to me on his way to the privy just as Aunt Ruth shouted, Bring me them other two pans on over here!

She'd begun fillin the one, and, careful to leave the soap cake and the little marble of bluein on the plank, I carried them tubs to her. Naw, she said, swingin the word testily upwards. I need them things in the water while I pump it. She was meanin the soap and the bluein.

So I run back to the plank to get em, catchin Delmer comin back from the privy. He leans down to me and whispers, I'll jist git me some bread and butter to eat in my hand. I looked up at him, grateful and relieved to hear it.

Aunt Ruth nodded her thanks to me, but then she begun to talk as she pumped the water. You know, I cain't believe I still have all these little uns. Sometimes it feels to me like I been takin care of children all of my life. I was the oldest of seven myself and helped raise them. Then me and Perry had us twelve—did you ever know that, Pat?

The first two died of croup as infants. Law, I like to never got over that. But then the Lord seen fit to gimme ten more, as healthy and live-ly as a nest of new birds thrivin and stretchin their necks. Now seven of them's done took their places in the world—even fourteen-year-old Pearl. Did you know Pearl's been taken on over at the Woolen Mills as a hander-inner?

What's a hander-inner?

She hands up threads to the women at the looms. She's been workin with your Mama, and Nell says she's real good at it.

Right then here come Granny Rule around the corner with a spring in her step. Ruth! she calls out, I done got me a poem started on the Night Riders an I need to borry a pencil from you. Listen to this. She stopped in front of us and looked up toward the treetops, like they was her audience.

Chapter One

Up the street they rode, full 200 strong
Meanin to demand their rights, and right a ancient wrong

Ruth had her to say it again, & then she said: Well Mama, I kindly like it—not that I think you ought to be firin up these younguns over all a that bidness. But I like how you say right an right. What if you's to say road an rode, too? Up the road they rode... Well, I ain't done it yet. But 13th Street ain't no road.

While they's arguin about where in the story the poem oughta begin, Delmer and the girls come back, and we was able to make our escape. He wanted to go straight over to the chute, but I said I aimed to cross over Broadway and not go next or near the place.

Why?

I don't know, I answered him. I jist don't wanna git up around all of them men. Then I asked him did he see the fire.

I seen it alright, he said kindly bitter-like, good as you *could* from my house. Soon as Ma seen all a them men she wouldn't let me move from the dern porch. So I need you to tell me all about it—exactly what happened—since I know *you* had a front row seat, little cuz. He put his hand on my head.

Much as I didn't care to be reminded that I was three years younger, and small for my age to boot, I figured Delmer was jealous about me seeing the Night Riders and couldn't resist the jab. When we got to 13th and Broadway Delmer stopped cold, and grabbed me by the strap of my overalls. I looked down towards the chute. There was even more men around it now than there had been before, and the photographer'd moved his camera around to the side to git a different angle on the scene.

Come on. Let's go down there, he said.

But my mind was made up. I give my head a sharp shake and I said, Newp. You can go if you want to, but I'm goin on over to Hollis's. I cut across Broadway on a diagonal. There was a Model T comin from the left, and a buggy comin from the right, so I trotted to the middle and then walked the rest of the way across. I glanced over my shoulder, and there was Delmer, follerin behind me with a frown on his face. It was a unusual feelin I had then, of the power my untold story give me.

Soon as we got over he said, Well, come on... what happened?

As we walked towards 8th Street through clouds of dust raised by the traffic on Broadway, I told him the whole glorious, terrifyin story of the Night Riders burnin down the chute. It was maybe the first time anybody had ever hung on my words so.

* * * * * * * * * *

Delmer and me was settin on a fallen tree near Red Duck Creek which run right alongside of Hollis's yard. Hollis was ever bit as amazed as Delmer to think Night Riders'd been marchin right under my window all night, but I could tell Delmer was gettin restless listenin to it a second time. When Hunter Hancock had finished deliverin his papers, he come ridin up the street on his pony, Dixie, and seen us there playing marbles. Delmer called to him, could he have a ride. Dixie was a big roan pony with white splotches all over her. Hunter said, Sure! and offered to let me and Hollis have one, too, but I knowed I couldn't, cause it was gettin on for noon by then, and I had to hightail it on home for dinner, Saturdays being a half day at the Woolen Mills.

Hunter lived at the other end of 8th Street where things got a little more upscale than they was beside Red Duck. Why catty-cornered across from the Hancocks' house, was Judge Wingate's big brick one with not jist one, but two porches on it. It was on a corner, and I reckon they was tryin to face 8th Street and College both. A big figure in town, the judge walked down 8th to the Courthouse ever'day, and he always wore him a bowler hat and carried a silver-topped cane.

The Schultz's house was a saggy, peelin clapboard full of kids. Hollis's daddy had been killed two years before in the war, while Miz Schultz was still expectin their seventh child, which turned out to be Hollis's whiney little brother, Albert. I knowed Hollis's darkest secret was that Mr. Schultz hadn't been killed in combat at all; he'd died of flu in camp. But I swore I'd never let on, cross my heart and hope to die, and I never did either, til right now. But with ever'body dead and gone I reckon it don't matter no more.

Hollis and me was still settin there when the screen door banged. We looked up and seen Miz Schultz at the forsythia that grew beside of their front stoop. She picked her out a good limber switch, broke it off, and stripped them blossoms off real clean between her thumb and forefinger. When she carried it back inside we could hear a thin pleadin rise up over the general squallin: *No Mama, don't!* Me, I was still staring at that bush, watchin the flurry of yellow petals sift down through it, the way pinfeathers does after a cat strikes.

* * * * * * * * * * *

It wasn't long after that we heard the noon whistle blow and I jumped up to go. I lit out for Water Street to stair-step my way home, goin left at this corner, right at the next, and so on. This route took me past the Woolen Mills—a long, red brick factory that always made me think of a river boat because of its twin black smokestacks that each ended in a jagged crown.

I run right into all the workers leavin the plant for the day, and ever'body was talkin about the Night Riders' invasion. I caught the tag-ends of a hundred conversations. Words like *witnesses, armed guards,* and *reward money* went flyin past my head til it was spinnin ever which way. One feller was sayin, My next-door neighbor was on the fire-wagon, and he said a gang of em stopped the wagon at gunpoint, sayin, *Stop where you're at or we'll blow you right through Berry Rule's Meat Market there. We aim for that chute to burn!*

At the mention of Uncle Berry I froze, but the man went on off in the wrong direction from the way I was goin. Still and all, there was plenty of other things bein said that I was wantin to hear.

…a meetin tonight of the Association, with Felix Ewing as the speaker! The tobacconists is gatherin over at Wilf Cutter's house…

…Ray Tibbs and that bunch readin in the newspapers about the Russian Revolution…

I hear tell Judge Wingate's fit to be tied.

Them tactics'll git em no place but in jail.

I was doin the best I could to keep all of these things in my head when I heard my name. I spun around and seen Papa, glarin at me like I done something wrong.

James Patrick Rule! What're you doin gawkin on the street corner like that? It was unusual for Papa to be hard with me, and I was surprised; he usually left that to Mama.

I… I don't know, Papa, I said, right nervous. I's jist goin home from Hollis's and…

Well you can walk with me. I happen to be goin that away, too.

He winked at me, so I felt better, but not much, cause he still didn't smile.

You seen your Mama?

Naw. But I jist heard some man…

Hardin! a voice called out behind us. Hardin Rule!

We stopped and turned around. It was Ellard Sanders, one of the owners of the Woolen Mills. He was great big around, and dressed up in Sunday clothes. There was a cigar between his teeth, smoked down near to a stub. The smell of it was powerful. He ambled up to us real slow-like.

Hardin, I hear you slept right through that ruckus last night.

I grinned up at Papa, waitin for him to set Mr. Sanders straight, but I couldn't catch his eye. Then he said, That's right, Mr. Sanders.

Well, you could've knocked me over with a feather, and Mr. Sanders too.

Amazing, he said. Why, with your house being so close and all I was certain you'd be able to help the authorities bring the right people to justice.

Papa shrugged his shoulders, as if to say he was real sorry.

The sheriff's offering a reward… um… were you aware of that?

Papa stared at him for a second, then without a word, turned and walked away. By the time we got to 13th Street I was huffin and puffin like a locomotive. We met Granny at the corner. She had the *DAILY LEAF* under her arm and a big smile on her face.

Hey there, y'all! I was jist on my way to show Berry today's paper. Looky here, right on the front page…

You ain't been talkin to no damn reporters, have you Ma?

I could tell by Papa's voice he was still in a bad mood, so I stayed quiet as I could while they talked.

Now listen here, son, there ain't no call to use profanity. They didn't print my name. I *told* em not to, and they didn't. Listen, all it says is: *A woman living directly across the street from the chute observed a band of unmasked men set fire to it at approximately midnight. They were all said to be from the northern part of Wills County.*

Papa groaned. Oh Ma, don't you see? Now they know we witnessed it. We cain't even pretend to've slept through it.

She heaved a big sigh and said, with one eye squinted up, If that's what you wanna do, what's stoppin you? It don't list our names nowhere in here.

It don't need to. Hell, who else lives *directly across the street from the chute?*

She turned away from him, and I was stricken to see that tears was ready to come. Papa softened some then. He took aholt of her arm real gentle-like and turned her back around.

Okay Ma, he said. Maybe it ain't too late. But you gotta promise me you won't mention last night again to another soul. There's gonna be trouble over this—a lot of trouble. I jist don't want you gittin mixed up in it. I don't want you hurt. Talkin about it's gonna put you—is gonna put *all* of us—right in the middle of this mess. Do you understand?

I understand, Hardin. And I promise I won't talk about it no more. She smiled a little, but I could tell she was hurt that he'd talked to her like she was a child. Then, soundin more like her old self, she said, But you cain't tell me not to talk to my own children about it.

No, Papa said as she started on towards Uncle Berry's grocery, but jist watch out who overhears you.

Granny walked off without another word, and we went on down the street to our house.

* * * * * * * * * *

At the table, Papa made Mama and us kids promise the same thing. Ever'body's gonna be askin us whether or not we seen it. And I want you to tell anybody that asks that we never heard a thing. Slept right through it. And don't bring it up with anybody that *don't* ask. Y'all hear me now? This is important.

We all agreed to keep quiet, though I still wasn't exactly clear on why. And I sure couldn't see no reason to mention to Papa that I'd already told Delmer and Hollis all about it. Bernard said Uncle Berry'd given him the selfsame lecture at the store that mornin—after he had Bernard tell *him* ever thing he'd saw. And Bridget Ruth hadn't seen nobody yet to tell it to.

But Papa, she said, with a little miffed expression on her face—prob'ly cause she'd missed her chance to tell about the most excitin thing that'd ever happened to us—you're tellin us to lie.

You're damn straight I am. You'll jist have to go to confession afterwards, or whatever y'all do. But don't go giving the priest no details. Now I mean you better do as I say, or you'll be breakin *another* commandment, *won't* you? Then he chuckled to himself.

Mama kept quiet, but her mouth drew up like a little string sack that was tied shut. See, she was Catholic and Papa was Methodist, and Papa had agreed when they got married that she could raise us kids Catholic, but ever once in a while he got in a little dig—not too bad a one, but a dig all the same.

I've got another question, Bridget Ruth said.

Papa grinned. You usually do. Go ahead.

What'd you mean last night when you said you don't see how Granny ever lived through the Civil War?

I could see Papa liked this question. He was finished eatin and he pushed his plate out of the way and leaned forward. Well, you know that both my parents was born and raised on farms near Panther Creek, east of town, out near Golo. Durin the Civil War most ever body out that way was for the Confederates. But her people, the Beans, was Union sympathizers. And so was her sweetheart at the time—Patrick Rule.

I blushed at this mention of my name, even though Papa pronounced it *Padrig*, as he said ever'body did all his daddy's life. I'd asked him about this once and he told me that was the way his parents said it, which was the Irish way, cause they was from Ireland.

So Patrick enlisted along with the Bean boys, to go fight for the Union.

For a second or two I imagined myself in a blue uniform, ridin a sleek horse to battle. But I never could get very far with daydreamin on the Civil War, cause I knew Mama's father—Granpa Touhey—had fought for the South. So I got muddled up no matter which side I pictured myself fightin on. Dreamin on the Great War was simpler. But it didn't much matter right then anyway, cause I wanted to hear the story Papa was tellin Bridget Ruth.

Granpap was damn near lynched for his Northern leanins at the height of the war, when Greenberry was taken over by Union soldiers.

You see, *because* Wills County was mostly for the South, the boys in blue who took over the town didn't exactly cover the Union in glory by the way they behaved. They was under a General Paine—now if *that* ain't a perfect name I never heard one—and he ordered em to shoot Southern sympathizers on sight. So it become real dangerous to be for the North around here...

Shoot! It wasn't safe to be for either side around here, Mama said in a disgusted tone.

Well now, it was a whole lot safer to be for the South in Wills County than for the North, Nell... you got to admit that.

Safe, my eye! she shot back. Why, the word don't enter into it. With Confederate sympathizers being shot right off the sidewalk? Don't talk to me about *safe*.

Aw hell, Papa said, settin up straight in his chair. How am I ever supposed to explain my story if you keep on mixin the children up this away?

Listen here, Hardin Rule, if you expect me to set quiet while you tell how safe it was to be for the South around here during the Civil War...

I was cuttin my eyes back and forth from Mama to Papa, waitin for the next explosion, and none too comfortable about it, when I noticed Bernard and Bridget Ruth smile at each other.

Alright, alright, Papa said finally. The plain truth is, you's liable to git your head shot off leanin one way as leanin the other, and that's a fact. But they was *pockets*, you see what I mean? Little pockets of people all over the county for the North or for the South. And over on Panther Creek was a pocket of people that didn't take kindly to Union sympathizers.

Now ever'body knew Granpap was for the North. And they might've let him by with it, too, cause they all loved him. Called him 'Uncle Billy' whether they's kin or not. But he was a kinda innocent old guy—a lot like his daughter over here next door as a matter of fact—and he was *interested* in the North/South question. Liked to talk about it and debate it, you see?

We nodded, and Papa lit him a cigarette and leaned forward on his elbows again. Well now, he musta been debatin away a little too hard one day, cause a gang of men dragged him over to a tree and set about to *lynch* him, by God. But his near neighbor stopped it, sayin, 'I cain't stand here and let you hang Uncle Billy.'

That was enough to turn the mob and bring em to their senses. Made em stop long enough to remember their own fondness for the old man, despite his politics. And they let him go.

But when the war was over, and Patrick Rule come riding home victorious to marry yore Granny… (Here I pictured my old Granny dressed up in white weddin finery and marryin a young soldier in blue) …why Granpap wasn't taking no chances. He'd seen that there was no end of trouble between neighbors who had took opposite sides, even once it was all supposed to be over.

What kind a trouble? Bernard asked.

Like midnight raids on one another's houses when they'd been into a bit a the old mule.

What's mule? asked Bridget Ruth.

Moonshine, Papa said with a grin. The pure-out kickin kind.

Did they kill each other in these raids? Bernard wanted to know.

Naw. They'd jist hoot and holler and call names and fire into the air. But it wasn't none too pleasant, all the same, and Granpap didn't want his daughter in the middle of that stuff. So he made em a weddin present of the farm I was raised on over by Hickory Grove, north of Greenberry. The selfsame place Ernest and Ola works now, right beside Ottus and them.

That's because Hickory Grove was a nest of N*orthern* sympathizers, Mama said, raisin one eyebrow.

That's right, my little magnolia blossom, Papa said, and we all laughed… well, all but Mama. But I felt easier now, cause I could see a little bit of a twinkle in her green eyes.

Anyhow, Granpap reckoned they'd be safer over there, which was smart on his part. So that's how come me and your Aunt Ruth and Uncle Berry and all *us* come to be raised up Hickory way, instead of on Panther Creek with all my cousins.

Me and Bernard nodded, but Bridget Ruth still wasn't satisfied. But you never said whether Granny herself was ever threatened during the Civil War.

Aw well, it was different for women… Papa began, but he cut off sharp when Mama scraped her chair back from the table real loud and

started clearin away the plates. Uh… not as I know of… but, I mean…
Aw *hell*, I'm jist sayin your Granny don't always understand when to
stay back and keep quiet. Like last night. Which brings me back to
where we started from. That mob burnin the chute—now that's one of
them times to stand back and keep your mouth shut.

Why exactly *did* they burn it, Papa? Bernard asked.

To try and force the high muckety-mucks that owns it to give em
a fair price for their tobacco. Now that's the last thing I'm gonna say
about that whole bidness—and I don't wanna hear another word
about it outa any of y'all either. It's closed, you hear me?

We nodded, real serious-like as Papa rose from the table. I saw him
pick up our copy of the *GREENBERRY DAILY LEAF* from the chair
beside the door, and carry it on out to the front porch swing. Me, I
went on out the back and made me some Tom-walkers outa tin cans
and string, and hobbled around on em, and did I don't know what all.
But when I come around the front again, Papa was still a-settin there
hangin over that newspaper for all he was worth.

Chapter Two

OLA LAWRENCE WAS FRETFUL. She put the children to bed in a no-nonsense manner and walked out towards the stable to do the evening milking. In the middle of the back yard she stopped, a hub in the circle of buildings that enclosed her life. Behind her the house, then sweeping clockwise, the privy, wagon shed, smokehouse, stable, and henhouse. Within the yard were chicken and calf pens. Beyond her fenced kingdom were woods, fields, the dark fire barn, creek and bottomland, pond and road.

She looked up at the sky. It was spotted with small purple clouds, a fresh, intermittent breeze sweeping them along like a lazy housekeeper. The sun was just down and dusk was having its brief, glorious way with the world. Later the moon would come up nearly full, which meant Ernest and the others would have plenty of light to return by, as long as that little breeze kept those clouds apart for them.

She carried on towards the stable. Better to keep herself occupied and not dwell on all that. Five months pregnant, Ola was about ready to have Ernest take over the milking.

It won't be long fore he'll *have* to, she muttered to Bertha, as she settled her stool into place beside the placid Jersey.

Soon she was humming Camptown Races with not a thought in her head as she worked. Physical sensation absorbed her completely: the teats in her hands, the regular rhythm of milking, the cow's warm bulk, rich smells of hay and animals, the changing music of the milk as the pail filled, and the kicking and squirming of the baby inside her. By the time she carried the pail through the dusk to the cistern, she was thoroughly quietened. Pouring the milk into the tall bucket, she covered it, tied the rope around its handle, and carefully lowered it until she felt the bottom touch the water. Then she covered the cistern, rinsed her hands at the washpan on the back porch, and took her gun down from the wall of the dogtrot to carry it inside for the night.

Ethelyn and Fred, who were almost three and almost four respectively, were sleeping like spinning tops when she hung the gun over the mantel. Thank goodness. All the same, she couldn't resist leaning over each bed and taking a deep whiff of their heads. Ola loved the smell of a sleeping child.

Lighting a coal oil lamp, she set herself up with her sewing basket at the table in the middle of the big room where they all slept. In winter they kept this table in front of the fireplace; in the summer it was moved out into the dogtrot, the long open breezeway between the two bedrooms of the house. It would soon be warm enough for that.

Ola had been a child of eight when her parents, Jake and Nettie Oakley, had bought this place from Granny Rule. She and her two sisters had slept with her parents in the room where she now sat sewing. Her four brothers had occupied the small room across the dogtrot.

Ernest had recently suggested that they install the children in that bedroom, as there would soon be three of them. But Ola had protested. They were still too young to be so far away from her in the night. She liked having the whole family close when they were sleeping. There was no hurry. Ernest had called her a mother hen and said she'd be keeping them all under her wings next; but it'd been said lightly, and he let her have her way.

Lora and Ottus, next door, used two bedrooms, but that was different. Their house was smaller and had no dogtrot. Lora, Ola's youngest sister, had married their next-door neighbor, Ottus Drew, four years back, the summer Ottus' daddy died. His mother, Ruth

Drew, had given them the farm and moved into town. Not long before, Ola had married Ernest and they'd begun to work this place. Since then Ola and Lora's lives seemed to follow a sort of rhyming pattern. Each couple had two children, first a boy, then a girl. And the two families had begun to share more and more of the farm work. Since Ernest played the fiddle and Ottus the guitar, the Drews and Lawrences got together nearly every Saturday night at one house or the other. The children prattled and played, the adults sang in soaring harmonies, and the whole thing floated on the rattling sweet blend of string music the two men had cultivated over the past four years.

But for all that Ernest and Ottus were quite different in temperament. Ernest, the older of the two by ten years, was very sociable and sought ways to do his work in the company of others whenever possible. Ottus, by contrast, was perfectly suited to the concentrated isolation of farming. Walking behind the plow, the mule's rump swaying, its tail switching flies, Ottus was content. There was no such thing as silence as far as he was concerned, with bugs and birdsong woven into the air around him. His mind was attuned to the task and did not wander.

No matter how much Ernest talked about the glories and ideals of the Planters Association, Ottus wouldn't consider signing up. Once when Ernest was trying to cajole him into joining this union of farmers, Ottus — never one to say much — began talking about his father.

When Daddy got that pain in his side the summer he died, Mama tried her best to git him to have the operation the doctor said he needed. Nothing she could say would make him change his mind. 'We ain't got the cash money for it,' he'd say, 'even if I *was* inclined to pay a man to stick a knife into me.'

When Ernest relayed this to Ola that night, she said, He was jist tryin to tell you he's like his daddy. He ain't gonna be told what to do, and joining the Association is, in a way, like joining the army or something. You got to do what you're told.

Shaking his head in disgust, Ernest had replied, It ain't whether you come up with the idea or someone else did that matters. It's whether the idea itself is right or wrong.

She had smiled at him.

Besides, he added, being in the company of people is jist more *fun* than standing off all by yourself.

Then she'd laughed, and so had he.

＊ ＊ ＊ ＊ ＊ ＊ ＊ ＊ ＊ ＊ ＊

This business of joining the Association was practically the only disagreement the two families had. It was why they weren't having a Saturday night singalong tonight. It was also the reason Ola had been so fretful earlier that evening. She hadn't slept well the night before, knowing Ernest was taking part in the raid on Greenberry. He had come home full of excitement in the middle of the night when she'd finally dropped off, and wanted to tell her all about it.

We tied our horses up by the creek on 13th Street and walked in a body towards the chute. There musta been two hundred men there, and there wasn't a shot fired nor nothing.

Ernest, she had said to him groggily, I'm jist glad you're back safe. You'll have to tell me the rest in the morning — I'm dog tired.

Then tonight he had left again, to go to the Association meeting at the Greenberry City Hall and hear Felix Ewing speak. He'd gone in with her brothers, Willie and Rudy, but that didn't make her feel any better about the possible dangers they might face in town tonight. Willie and Rudy were hardly a safeguard against trouble, being far more likely to stir it up. So she had been nervous all evening, and the nervousness returned as she sat at her sewing.

When she finally heard a wagon on the road, her heart leapt, and she went out to the front steps and saw Ernest coming through the gate. He waved jauntily to her as he drove around the house to the stable, and she knew it was alright. After putting the horse to bed he came into the room and marched straight over to her.

Come here and kiss your man, Ola Lawrence! he said with a grin.

She did so, drawn equally, as ever, by his vitality and his blonde good looks.

You shoulda been there, Oleo!

Well now, I don't imagine there was too many women there.

One or two—but you're right, all the pretty ones stayed home. Ewing was splendid—he's everything they say. No wonder they call him the Moses of the Black Patch. He started out by sayin real stern-like, *Such violations of law and order as Greenberry saw last night in the burning of its tobacco chute, such drastic measures, must be publicly condemned by this Association!*

Ola motioned for him to lower his voice, then whispered, He didn't!

Why sure he did, said Ernest a little more quietly. He has to. And all he said there, if you listen careful, is that they must be *publicly* condemned. Which they must. Don't mean he actually believes they're wrong. Oh I tell you, Ola, he's a master. You shoulda heard the crowd—they went nuts cheering him. When I jumped to my feet Rudy scowled at me. He thought it was crazy to go into town at all today; but I told him, 'Rudy my friend, this meetin's been advertised for weeks. If nobody was to show up for it *that's* what'd be dangerous. We got to act like last night never happened.' Oh it was something....

What else did Ewing say?

Ernest stood in front of the fireplace as if he were the union leader: *We tobacco farmers enjoyed welcome prosperity in the 1919 market. The War in Europe, which many of you supported in the flesh, and which some of your people supported with their lives, helped spread around the world the taste for tobacco grown in western Kentucky and Tennessee. This is no surprise, for there is no finer tobacco available!* Here, of course, everybody was on their feet again and cheering. He waits for us to settle down before he says, *Thank you, but I speak only the truth. However, this year is a different matter, as you know only too well. This year the market has fallen, and we are no longer being offered a fair price for our crops. Fifteen years ago, gentlemen, Black Patch farmers faced a similar plunge in prices, engineered by the capitalist buyers, who were happy to let us do all the work while they enjoyed all the profits. We saw then that the way to fight the big boys is to be bigger than them. Now, how can small farmers be bigger than the big buyers?*

And before he could say another word, Ray Tibbs roars out, 'By standin together!' Ewing points at Ray and says, *By standing together! That's right. That is the only way! And what's more, I propose we re-design the market itself to give the growers more control. We must go a step further than the old union policy of storing our tobacco and holding it off the market until a fair price is offered. This Association must begin to run its own market, operating a loose leaf floor sales system. We must cut out the big-business-dominated middle men — the so-called tobacconists — and take control of the sales ourselves! We aim to do nothing less than hold the buyers in the calloused palm of our hands!*

Ola smiled and shook her head.

Everybody was on their feet and yelling and then come the icing on the cake. He says, *We MUST stand together. The very Commonwealth of Kentucky holds nothing less as its motto: United we stand, divided we fall. Say it with me, all of you, and mean every word!* So we all chanted it together a couple times, then the band strikes up My Old Kentucky Home, and we all stayed on our feet and sung it through, but slow-like. I swear Ola, it was like I'd never heard it before. Listen to this.

Ernest reached for his violin, which he kept hanging on the wall, and began to play the song for the lament that it is. After he played it through once and she caught onto the pacing, she began to sing along, and she could hear for the first time that it is about slaves being driven from the land they love — sold away from it by the rich, who owned them. When the song finished she looked at him with tears shining in her eyes, and was glad all over again that she'd married him.

✳ ✳ ✳ ✳ ✳ ✳ ✳ ✳ ✳ ✳ ✳ ✳

At church the next morning Brother Walker stayed with his text of Jesus's last days on earth, it being the Sunday before Easter. He made no reference to the burning of the chute, though he knew some of his colleagues in town planned to denounce it as unChristian behavior.

Ola didn't know whether Ernest was expecting Brother Walker to come out and publicly support the Association or not, but she was relieved, for Lora and Ottus' sake, that he hadn't brought it up. She glanced over at Lora, but her younger sister was busy with Harry, who was squirming on her lap. Adell grinned at her over Ottus's shoulder. As soon as Meeting was over, Harry scurried towards Fred, and the two of them ran outside to play.

The congregation filed past Brother Walker. The country minister was six feet, two inches tall, with silver hair, intense blue eyes, and a hawk nose, all of which lent him unusual dignity. He taught school to supplement his income, and so was not directly involved in farming, as were many preachers in Wills County.

Mornin, Brother Walker. Fine sermon, Ola said, and passed on. Ernest did the same, then they joined Ola's brothers, Willie and Rudy Oakley and their wives, who stood talking near the field where the vehicles were parked. There were mostly wagons, with a few buggies and one or two trucks.

Well, Ernest, have you heard the latest? asked Rudy, cutting a chew from his twist and tucking it inside his jaw. Willie followed suit.

You mean since last night's meeting in town? Ernest tapped a cigarette from the pack in his shirt pocket, and lit up.

Yeah. Ray Tibbs rung up Asa this mornin and asked him to spread the word. The tobacconists are all camped out in Wilf Cutter's house ready for all-out war, seems like.

They got their wives and children across the street in Harley Adams' house, and got armed guards surrounding both properties! This was from Willie, the most excitable of the Oakleys. The others shushed him and looked around. I tell you this thing is jist gittin going, he whispered. It's liable to end up no *tellin* where!

Ola noticed that Ottus had ushered Lora and the children into their wagon. The two sisters waved to each other, a silent acknowledgement of the undercurrent of tension in their glance.

What else did Ray say? asked Ernest. Ray Tibbs was the leader of the local Night Riders.

He says we're all to meet at his store tomorrow mornin at ten, Rudy answered.

While the men talked, Ola stood nearby with her two sisters-in-law, Faye and Joetta. Y'all gonna be able to join us next Sunday for Easter dinner? Mama's comin, and Hazel n Earl. Oh and of course Lora and Ottus.

I done promised my folks we'd have Easter with them, said Rudy's wife, Faye, without apology.

Sure, Ola, said Joetta, who was always anxious to avoid a scene. Me and Willie and our two'll be glad to come.What can I bring? A pie'd be nice, thanks Joetta. And maybe some of them oysters you fix. Ernest loves oysters. I ain't had too much mornin sickness this time around, but working with oysters might jist start it up, if you know what I mean.

Joetta laughed nervously, and looked up to see that Willie had started towards the wagon without her. Oh—better go. See y'all next Sunday.

* * * * * * * * * * *

The next morning, Ola gathered a dozen candled eggs into her basket and took a due bill from under the flour sifter to exchange for groceries. Ernest helped her onto the wagon bench, and then handed Ethelyn up for her to cradle as best she could on what was left of her lap. Fred clamored into the back and held onto the side panel.

I'm gonna stand up! he said.

Oh no you're not, Fred Leonard Lawrence, Ola returned over her shoulder. You'll set down or else you'll ride up here beside me.

Aw, cain't I stand up, Daddy?

You heard your mama, Fred. Set down.

As the wagon bounced them over the gravel roads, Ola thought perhaps Fred was right; it probably would be more comfortable to be standing. Sure will be nice when we can afford a buggy with a spring seat, she called to Ernest.

One of these days… he answered, smiling. Ola marveled once again at her luck in having married a good-natured man. Rudy or Willie would've snapped their wives heads off for a comment like that.

She hadn't known Ernest all her life, as Lora had Ottus. The Lawrences had farmed just east of Pottsville, only four or five miles away from the Oakley place, but far enough away that she never met him until 1914. Unable to go to war because of something Dr. Barton called a pigeon chest, he had been helping to run a war bond rally at the Pottsville Methodist Church. With Willie and Rudy both in the war, Ola and her mother had gone to it. Ola had been struck immediately by the tall, handsome man with the affable manner; and he had clearly been struck by her. They were married within a year, and that first impression she'd had of him had been borne out in their daily lives.

Ernest, I want you to take me over to Berry Rule's Meat Market. I'd rather do my shoppin there than be under foot at this meeting. Lora told me she was visiting her mother-in-law today, so I'll put in my order and then go on over to Miz Drew's and wait for you there.

Well, alright. I reckon there wouldn't be much you could do at Ray's, excepting go upstairs and visit with Maudie.

I ain't fixing to climb no stairs with Ethelyn and Fred—not in my condition.

Cain't say as I blame you for that, Oleo.

As they slowed down to take the corner beside Tibbs' Grocery, a half-circle of men had already gathered. Whoa there, Ernest! Ray called out.

Ernest reined in the horse and drew up alongside the group. Ola rolled her eyes. Why couldn't he just have called out that he'd be back?

Looks like a auspicious occasion, Ray.

A what-spicious occasion, did you say, Ernest? James January called out from behind Ray, and the others laughed.

That was a good'n, Cluster Higgins said.

We got important business to discuss, Ernest. Aren't you coming? Ray Tibbs tended to be a serious, task-oriented individual, especially where the Association was concerned. He considered himself a Populist, part of a great tradition of agrarian reform, and had probably read more books than all the rest of the men present put together. He had read everything he could find on the Russian Revolution, as well as on all the unions which were being organized around the world in the post-war climate. His grocery was

on the northern edge of Greenberry, and in addition to running it
he also raised five acres of tobacco.

I'll be here, Ray, don't git your apron in a knot. Some of the
men laughed at this, as Ray was wearing his grocer's apron. I jist
have to drop the family off in town and I'll be right back.

Ray smiled then, and waving to Ola as he turned back to the
group of men in front of his store, pulled out his watch to check
the time.

* * * * * * * * * * *

Rule's Meat Market was a long, dark grocery with a creaking
wood floor, empty except for the counters along the sides and at the
back. On the left side was candy, canned goods and fresh vegetables;
along the right were staples, a barrel of pickles, and one of crackers;
the counter at the rear was for meat. Today there were about five or
six customers at any one time in a steady coming and going.

Berry was busy behind the meat counter, so Ola waited. She
had to lift Fred, and then Ethelyn up to see what was in the candy
case. Finally he came around to take her order. After she had
asked for the usual coffee, flour, sugar and such, with a pepper-
mint stick for Ethelyn and a horehound stick for Fred, she asked
whether Lora and Ottus had been in yet that day.

Yes'm, Ola, they were here about half an hour ago I reckon, but
I believe they've gone over to my sister's place now.

Thank you, Berry. I'll pick this stuff up in a while then. Ernest's
at a ... uh... Ernest'll be along in a while.

Berry knew Ernest was a Night Rider, and deduced from Ola's
slip that they were meeting somewhere right now, no doubt to
decide what to do next. The newspaper that morning had carried strong denunciations of Friday night's raid from the town's
leading citizens, most notably Judge Arch Wingate, who vowed
to bring the chute burners to justice. They quoted the judge as
saying, These hooligans'll stop at nothing, until they stop in front
of my bench!

The court was due to convene its spring session in two weeks
and the case of the Night Riders would be first on the docket. Ber-

ry gave Ola a neutral smile and said, That'll be fine. Your order'll be ready when you come for it.

Sweeping Ethelyn up in her arms and calling to Fred to come along, she walked the two blocks to Ruth Drew's house. Ruth was not only Lora's mother-in-law, but she had been the Oakleys' neighbor throughout Ola's childhood. Ola knew she wouldn't mind them waiting at her house for Ernest.

They were sitting around the kitchen table drinking coffee, and Ottus lifted Harry off of a chair to make room for Ola. Fred and Harry scrambled out the back door to play, their mothers calling to them to stay in the yard. Ethelyn joined Adell, who was toying with spools on the floor.

Much obliged, Miz Drew, said Ola, as Ruth handed her a cup of coffee. Oh my, but it feels good to set down.

When's that baby due? Ruth asked.

July, jist like *all* of mine.

Funny how that works, ain't it? Four of mine was winter babies, and three come in the spring. Seems like family birthdays always comes in clusters that away.

Ottus began to shift a little, uncomfortable with the direction of the conversation. Before Ola came in they'd been talking about the Night Riders, and Lora had asked whether Granny Rule mentioned seeing Ernest among the men who burned the chute. Just then Ola had knocked, and as she went to answer the door Ruth had whispered, She didn't call his name.

They sat for a moment in uncomfortable silence, uncertain whether or not to bring up the subject which occupied all their minds. Ruth had counselled them not to repeat anything she told them about witnessing the incident—'not even to Ernest and Ola.' Lora had felt a twinge of indignation at this—her mother-in-law telling her not to talk to her own sister, when it was clear Ruth had discussed it with *her* family.

They all looked at the newspaper, which was folded in the middle of the table. Finally Ola smiled and said, Miz Drew, would you mind if I looked at your paper? We don't take it and…

Ruth sighed with resignation and said, Course not, Ola. Help yourself.

As she read, the others shot frowning glances at each other. The front page carried three articles on the issue. One was a rehash of the events as reported in Saturday's paper. Another described the Association rally and highlighted Felix Ewing's remarks. The third was an inflammatory piece outlining the angry concerns of the tobacconists, and their response to the raid. Not only were armed guards posted around their homes and warehouses, but Judge Wingate was asking Governor Morrow to send in the National Guard as extra protection during the grand jury investigation set for next week. Any witnesses to the action were strongly urged to come forward in aid of the investigation.

After reading the last article, Ola looked up at the others, her eyes wide. The National Guard? she said.

Ottus suddenly stood up and, stepping over the two little girls, opened the back door. I'm gonna go keep a eye on the boys.

Chapter Three

PAPA TOSSED THE *GREENBERRY DAILY LEAF* onto the table the Thursday evening after the chute burnin and declared that the whole town'd gone crazy as a loon. It was rainin out—had been all day long—and the house felt smaller than usual somehow, what with the constant noise on the roof and ever'body being cooped up indoors.

It ain't enough that we're setting around waitin for the army to march in here and take us over. Now the town council's done voted to remove... At this point Papa interrupted hisself and busted out laughing like he couldn't help it, ...to remove the damn hitch-racks from around the square. He sat back and guffawed til he was wiping away tears. None of us dared say a word; we jist stared at him.

Mama and Bridget Ruth was washin the dishes. Bernard had picked up the paper soon's Papa dropped it and was readin it like he hadn't never seen a newspaper before. Mama'd jist handed me the milk pitcher and told me to throw the rest of it over the back porch railin, sayin it'd gone blinky since *somebody*—she's lookin at me of course, though I never done it—forgot to put it back in the icebox that mornin.

After a minute I went on ahead and throwed the milk out. When I come back in, ever'body was still quiet, so I handed the pitcher up to Mama and said, Well, they'll put new ones up, won't they? Otherwise, where's ever'body supposed to hitch their mules and horses?

Papa, who'd recovered hisself, pointed a finger at me and said, Here stands a boy smarter'n the government. Naw, Pat, the sad truth is they don't aim to put up new ones. What they aim to do is draw a line in the sand between the town folks and the country folks—now that's jist what they're aimin to do with *this* little move.

I was tryin to figure out about the sand when Mama said, Well, I have to say, it don't make no sense, when more'n half the people around the square still uses buggies and wagons.

Hell yes it makes sense, if what you're aimin to do is make things hard for people from out in the county. Why it's jist... it's a *ins*ult is what it is. It's like sayin if you don't drive a automobile, you don't exist.

It's gonna be interestin to see what people've got to say about it, Mama said, taking off her apron and comin over to set down at the table.

It sure is. And they've picked a interestin time to make this little move, too. Jist when all them farmers is bein threatened with jail over the chute burning.

What they're forgittin is that Greenberry is the county seat. It ain't here jist for the town folks, Mama said. Neither she nor Papa was town bred, and at times like these it showed. They was both raised up on farms. Papa's family had moved into town when he was nineteen. Mama had moved in to work at the Woolen Mills when she was seventeen or thereabouts. She and her sister, Bridgie, had boarded over at Miz Hayden's, who was still runnin her boardin house over on 10th and Broadway.

Bernard was pointin out how a big part of Uncle Berry's trade come from farmers, and the three of them seemed set to talk on. So when Bridget Ruth made a move for the front porch swing, I follered her.

It was still rainin buckets. We settled ourselves all cozy, rockin back and forth at the edge of the storm. I pulled my feet up and hugged my knees, and let her do the swingin. The water sheetin off the roof in front of us seemed to make a curtain around our own private world. When we'd git a big clap of thunder and lightnin ever once in a while, it'd thrill us half to death. Settin out on the porch during a storm was one of our favorite things to do.

After awhile I told Bridget Ruth what Virgil West'd said to me at school that day, about the Night Riders sending out warning notes.

*Warn*ing notes, she said. Who to?

He said Judge Wingate got one in his mailbox yesterday mornin, and so did Dick Dunsmore, the auctioneer from the chute.

What'd they say?

The one to Dick Dunsmore said he's to quit workin at the chute or suffer the conquer—I don't know, suffer something.

Suffer the consequences, said Bridget Ruth, gittin all excited. I bet it said *or suffer the consequences*. That's what warning notes always say.

What does it mean?

It's like saying *or else*. It means they're gonna git you if you don't do what they say. Did anybody sign it? Did it say *Night Riders* at the bottom?

Virgil said it said, *signed The Committee*.

We swung in silence for awhile. Then Bridget Ruth said, I went by the drugstore after school on Tuesday and Lydia Washam was in there tellin ever'body how she'd seen the Night Riders go right by her house. She's so rich and pretty. I'd give anything to be her.

You wouldn't wanna be no tobacconist's daughter, Bridget Ruth.

Well… I suppose not. But I sure wouldn't mind being rich. She's got the prettiest clothes, and you know how their house has all them cut glass windows around the front and side?

Which one's their house. Is it that red brick one jist off the square down from the Water an Light building?

That's the one, Bridget Ruth said all dreamy-like. Jist think what it woulda been like seein the whole thing through *cut glass* windows—the horses and the torchlight all fractured up like in a kaleidoscope. Lydia said it was almost romantic. She said they were wearin capes made from bedsheets and…

Aw that ain't so. She makin the whole thing up—I bet you she never seen em at all. *We* seen em, and they wasn't wearin no bedsheets. Not even masks. Jist had their coats on inside-out is all.

No she didn't make it up, cause it turns out Clayton Tyrell's mother made the costumes for em, and Lydia says *her* mother says she'll wear her out if she ever catches Lydia speaking to Clayton again.

Aw hogwash! Them Night Riders ought to've taught her daddy a lesson that night.…

Well, she said they phoned em up in the middle of the whole thing. See, there she goes again. They couldn't have phoned em. How could they when the Telephone Exchange'd been took over? Taken. Because, Mr. Know-it-all, they were the ones that took it over. Now, are you gonna let me tell this story, or would you rather jist not hear it?

Go on. I'm a-listenin.

Lydia said the whole family was standin there in the dark watching the Night Riders go past, when all of a sudden the telephone rang behind em in the living room. They bout jumped out of their skins. Her daddy went over and answered it, and a voice said, 'Mr. Washam, your tobacco warehouse is on fire.' She said her daddy waited for a minute and then said, 'Hell, let it burn.' Said the rest of the family could hear the laughter inside the receiver all the way across the room, til her daddy hung up and *squashed* it.

Squashed it?

Squashed that laughter.

Why'd he say to let it burn?

He reckoned they was only tryin to draw him out of the house so they could give him a beatin. And Lydia said it turned out he was right—the Washam warehouse wasn't touched. But that wasn't the best part. She said after that her mother went over to a fancy desk full of little drawers that she has. Lydia says one of the drawers was always kept locked and nobody, not even Mr. Washam, ever knew what was inside of it. Whenever anybody'd ask about it she'd jist say, 'That's none a your beeswax.' But that night, she took a key out of a vase on the mantel and unlocked the drawer, opened it up, and pulled out a little bitty *gun*!

I'd been listening all along, but now I got real interested.

Lydia called it a pearl-handled derringer. Then she said her mother aimed it at each one of them, for all the world like she's gonna shoot em, and when they jumped back she laughed and said, 'Ain't it jist the prettiest little thing you ever did see?' Her husband said, 'Jackie, give that to me! You don't know how to use a gun!' But she said, 'Oh yes I do. I could shoot you all, any day I want. I had lessons a long time ago, and you needn't think I'm prepared to stand around here defenseless while a gang of outlaws threatens us and our livelihood.'

I'd never heard tell of a woman's pistol before, but I could imagine it alright.

Then she said her mother turned to Robbie, Lydia's little brother…
I know who Robbie is!

She says to him, 'I've kept that drawer locked all these years mostly for fear of you. Now this is not *for* you, young man. It's my pistol, and if I ever catch you next or near it, I swear I'll wear you out, do you hear me?'

That made me laugh, picturing Robbie. I bet he said yes'm right quick.

Ain't that the most amazin story? Would you ever think it to look at Miz Washam?

What happened next?

Nothin, I reckon. They all went off to bed.

What about the Night Riders?

She said they'd gone by then, and didn't bother em no more. But the next day Mr. Washam got armed guards to watch their house night and day. They been there ever since.

While Bridget Ruth was tellin about Lydia Washam the rain had slackened off to a pattering. About the time it stopped altogether, Mama come to the door and called us in to go to bed. As we went in I thought I heard the groan of Granny's front porch swing next door. But it was too dark to be sure, and it coulda jist been the wind, so I didn't call out.

* * * * * * * * * *

The next day was a half day at school because it was Good Friday. The re-buildin of the chute had begun, and the poundin of nails through planks was about to drive ever'body crazy.

After dinner I run over to Delmer's to see what he wanted to do. Granny showed up, half addled with the noise. She'd stuffed her ears full of cotton, but she yelled that it still felt like they's hammerin them nails right into her skull bone. Aunt Ruth declared that ever train that went through was a blessin cause the noise of the train was a nicer way to go deaf than this other. The thing about grown-ups is that when somethin's happening, they think it's only happenin to them. They kept on explainin about this noise like we couldn't hear it.

Delmer and me decided to git out of Boxtown altogether. He suggested we go cut us some shinny sticks in the woods north of town, and we lit out. George Adams, one of the colored kids in the neighborhood, trailed along with us. We cut through the big yard of the Enterprise Barn—the biggest tobacco barn of all and the one where dances was usually held—to git to the railroad track. There was men with rifles on ever side of ever warehouse, but they didn't seem to pay us no mind.

Did y'all see them Night Riders the other night? George asked, and me and Delmer looked at one another.

Naw, said Delmer. Did you?

George lived down by the creek beyond 13th and Depot.

Oh yes, I seen em. They come right past our house on their horses, and then they got off and tied the horses to the trees beside the crick, and walked up the middle of the street to the chute. They's *hondreds* of em. How could you not've saw em, Pat? Your house is right there.

I cain't tell you how much it pained me to have to pretend that George had saw more'n me of the Night Riders' raid, so I crossed my fingers, and said, I don't know, jist slept through it. I kept them fingers all twisted up, in plain sight—both hands, but George didn't notice. He jist kept on tellin all about it as we walked along the railroad track.

When we come up towards Ray Tibbs' Grocery we heard loud talkin. Sounded like some sorta argument. There wasn't no chairs out front of the store like usual, and at first we couldn't figure out where it was coming from, but we recognized Ray Tibbs' voice alright, and ever'body knowed he was the head of the Night Riders.

Let's play like we're spies, I whispered, and the three of us crossed the Paducah Road that run alongside of the tracks, and we cut into the Tibbs' side yard. Soon's we got up against the house behind a row of hydrangea bushes, we could tell he was on the upstairs screened-in porch, and it was his wife he was talkin to.

Alright then, you go on over with the girls and I'll stay home if that's how everybody feels about it.

Ray, I've just... I've got to the point where I don't know what's best to do.

You know what, it's always this sorta stuff that holds a man back. There never was a damn revolution yet that didn't get stalled by somebody's mother begging a man to 'just act nice.' Now, I ain't talkin about you, Maudie, you know that.

Things went quiet for a minute, and we was about to give up on spyin when we heard the magic words.

Ray, I knew who you were when I married you. I reckon that's a good part of *why* I married you. I didn't foresee this *Night Riding* business, but I knew you were a firebrand like everybody said, and I always knew you wouldn't be satisfied just to make a living and raise a family like everybody else. You could only be happy if you were part of some larger effort to make things better—whatever form that might take. Your grandmother can say all she wants to about not allowing you in to her funeral...

We couldn't believe it, but the two of em actually laughed a little at this. Then Miz Tibbs went on.

I trust you, Ray. It's some of these others and the way they get all het up that I don't care for. You're an idealist, so you give em the benefit of the doubt, but *I* think they're just looking for trouble.

George'd picked up a roly-poly bug and was playin with it.

Maudie, I can control Rex and Lubie and that bunch. You can't ever get a group of men together but you won't have a couple of hotheads among em.

What about Willie Oakley? Delmer and me looked at one another. He worries me, too. He just doesn't seem quite right in the head somehow.

It was all we could do not to bust out giggling at this. We put our hands over our mouths and commenced to shakin all over, and George whispered, What'd she say? That sobered us up right quick, cause they'd stopped talkin and we was sure they'd heard us. But then they started again.

I know what you mean about Willie, but I think he's harmless enough. I believe the war agitated his nerves some, but he's got Rudy...

Rudy's not much better if you ask me.

That's true I guess. But Ernest is a good influence on em. I set a lot of store by Ernest Lawrence. He's a good man.

Yeah, I like him, what I've seen of him. Why do you think it is that the Oakley girls are so normal and pleasant, and their brothers so...

Course, then there's Hazel.

Oh, I'd forgot she's their sister. That's right.

Yeah, poor old Hazelnut. You know, come to think of it, maybe it wasn't just the war that got to Willie. Hell, maybe there *is* a trace of insanity runs through that family.

Jessie Lemon works the sewing machine right next to Hazel over at the Woolen Mills, and she says Hazel keeps tee-totally silent over there.

Yeah I've heard that... Won't talk to anybody but herself.

Oh, it's pitiful really. We've got enough to worry about with our own crazy family without talking about poor Hazel Smith. Ray, I've decided what we'll do. We'll just have Easter dinner here by ourselves. If Nannie doesn't want you, she can't have any of us.

You sure, Maudie? Not that I worry about Nannie, but it's gonna be hard on the girls.

Nonsense. They'd rather be off with their friends than with family anyway. You'll see, they'll be fine. Now you go on down and take over the store from em. I've got baking to do, and by now they'll be wanting to run off and visit Shirley or Violet til supper. Tell em we'll eat at six, when you close up.

We could hear they was about done talkin, so we got up and went on our way, kindly disgusted with the leader of the Night Riders gittin all worked up about stuff like family dinners. And calling his grandmother *Nannie!* Crimonently. Looked like spying wasn't as interesting as cuttin shinny sticks after all. Fact it was downright disappointin.

* * * * * * * * * *

That night after supper we all set out on Granny's porch awhile. It was Papa's idea to go over. He said he thought she needed some cheering up. The temperature was real pleasant, and the rain held off. Bridget Ruth set between Papa and Granny in the swing, and Bernard and me took the chairs. Mama went down the sidewalk to talk to Klute Walker for awhile. When she got back she took my chair and I set down on the top step and leaned against the bannister, rollin three or four migs from my pocket around in the palm of my hand. I liked ever'thing about marbles, the colors of em, the little chinkin sounds they made rocking against each other, and the cobbly feel of em against your palm.

Papa was teasing Granny about her chickens. Them girls' combs is gittin mighty red I notice. Won't be long til you'll have you a whole new flock running around. Now, looks to me like you oughta go into the egg bidness, Mama. Why you'd make a fortune off of them chickens of yours.

Aw I done had enough of all that to suit me a lifetime, Hardin.

Why do you bother with chickens at all then, Granny? asked Bernard, winkin at Papa.

We all knowed Granny kept em for pets. All of this palaver was jist to lead her into talkin about her chickens, cause she was so comical with em.

I jist like em is all. Hercules is the prettiest rooster any of y'all's ever saw, now go ahead and admit it.

I don't know, Granny, said Bridget Ruth. That'n of Aunt Ruth's is kinda showy with his white, white feathers.

Aw! That common old Leghorn? she said, pretending to be offended. Why he ain't a patch on my Hercules. Pat, run around the back and git him for me. Y'all ain't seen his new trick I done taught him.

Granny, he won't come for nobody but you, I said. I been bit by that derned old rooster more'n once. Well, this set em all to laughin, but I stuck to my guns. I ain't a-kiddin. He's mean, cept to Granny.

They kept up their teasing, but I held my ground on this one. I didn't care if they said I was chicken of chickens or not. I wasn't going near that Hercules.

Finally Granny went and got him herself. She cut through the house, and come back onto the porch carryin that rooster, a-pettin and talkin to him like he's her firstborn son. It tickled Mama and Papa both half to death. He was a colorful bird, all red and black with a big old droopy fern of a green tail on him, and I did have to admit he was pretty—but only to myself.

Mama had moved into the swing to give Granny more space. She set down, and the rooster got all cosy in her lap. Hercules, she said, all sweet-talk and strokin, you member how I taught you to crow for me?

Ever'body groaned and carried on like they couldn't believe this one, but she says, Now never mind them. They'll preciate you as much as I do once you show em how smart you is, now won't they, my fine feller? Granny wants you to crow for her. Go on, Hercules, you show em. Er-er-er. Soon as she made a little low crowing sound, he rared back an let off one that probably had ever'body in the neighborhood checkin their watches.

Well we all thought that was pretty cute sure nough, and we carried on a right smart. Granny was jist a-beamin at Hercules, and I looked up and seen the selfsame expression on Papa's face, cept he was lookin at her. Bernard asked Granny if he could try it, and she said he could of course, but soon's he reached over for him, dang if that cussed old bird didn't nip him in the wrist.

Bernard set sucking on his wound for a minute. Then he looked ol Hercules right in his beady little eyes an said, Jist you wait, you Sunday dinner on two legs. Your day's a-comin. I'll git the last laugh yet.

Granny give Bernard a look like she's shocked, and hugged Hercules up against her bosom, sayin, Don't you listen to that, sugar pie.

And Papa says, That's right, Hercules. Why, when the good Lord calls you to that big old barnyard in the sky, don't you worry none, cause I know a fella can stuff you real pretty—and I don't mean with oyster dressin.

Granny said, *Do you?* so enthusiastic-like that Hercules give out another crow, and we liked to died laughing. It was specially good to see Granny havin fun. She hadn't been herself since they burnt the chute an Papa give her such a dressing down about mixing into it. I thought things was back to normal.

Chapter Four

LORA DREW SAT IN THE DOGTROT of her sister's house, chibbling cornbread for the Easter dinner dressing. Ola was across the table chibbling biscuits, her belly swollen beneath her apron. The older of the two by eight years, Ola was a self-assured woman whose delicate, heart-shaped face sometimes deceived strangers into thinking she was of a delicate nature and constitution as well. Though both women had brown hair, Lora's was darker, and set off a spirited, almost impudent face and manner. Looking at them, one would never guess that Lora was the shyer of the two outside their family circle.

The day was clear, though still slightly glazed from yesterday's rain. A shallow puddle or two shone silver in the sun on the driveway, and on the road beyond the gate. Ola's chickens stepped and pecked about the yard, their segmented motion like bright embroidery stitches across the scene.

I miss this old dogtrot, said Lora. Wish me and Ottus had us one on our house.

Ola laughed. Well, seein as how the house was sorta built around the dogtrot, I don't think it's something you could add on later.

You could if you jist generally knocked a hole through your house, Lora mused.

Ola laughed again. Naw, I know what you mean though. It's so cool and nice in the hot weather, I don't know what we'd do without it. And look at us settin out here in early April, enjoying the sunshine. She stopped crumbling the bread for a moment and drew from the pocket of her sweater a small, octagonal tin box with orange and yellow flowers painted all over it. We've had so much rain here lately, seems a shame not to git outside when the sun shows itself. Dipping the snuff with a frayed sprig of sassafras, Ola tucked it inside her lower lip.

Bertha the Jersey, and the Lawrences' three Herefords grazed in the field beyond the front fence, where Harry and Fred were playing. Adell and Ethelyn sat near their mothers on the porch steps, cooking their own feast of mud and grass in old Calumet baking powder cans.

Have you counted up how many you'll have here tomorrow? asked Lora.

Well, let's see: there's you and Ottus and the kids, that makes four; added to me and Ernest of course, so eight; and Mama's coming, and Willie and Joetta and their two, that's... uh... thirteen; Rudy and them's going over to Faye's folks, but Hazel and Earl'll be here... so I reckon we'll be fifteen altogether.

Lordamercy, said Lora, shaking her head. It'll be like old times around here. Be like it was growing up in this house—bodies ever'where.

Oh it'll be fun, Ola said, smiling. Then, spitting into the coffee can beside her chair, she added, Long as none of em starts on Mama about the homeplace.

As long as none of em starts on you and *Ernest*, you mean. I swear, it galls me how they are over it. They ever one made their choice to move off way before Mama ever passed it to y'all.

I know. But I guess they don't see it that away. They think me and Ernest sweet-talked her outa the place somehow. The fact that we support Mama with a third of the crop ever year, like you and Ottus does with Miz Drew, that don't seem to count for much with some of em. But you know Lora, I'm determined to smooth it over for the sake of all our kids. I'd hate for this bad feeling to go into the next generation. It's like poison.

Aw Ola, it won't. They git along great. Why, Rudy's little Bethy jist loves Ethelyn to pieces, and my Adell too.

I know it. Bethy's coming over next Saturday and gonna stay the night so she'll be here for our singalong. I invited all of em, but Faye said she could only send Bethy, cause they had so much to do gittin her Mama moved in with her sister over near Richard Creek. Poor little old youngun was so sorry about missin Easter out here with us that Faye decided to let her come Saturday.

Well, said Lora, standing up to brush the crumbs from her lap, my chibbling fingers is about wore out. I've done three pans a cornbread. What's next?

Let's go see if there's enough chicken liquor to wet all this bread down good. Ummm, them hens is startin to smell mighty good, if I do say so myself.

When the two women went inside, Ethelyn said in a business-like tone, Well, I'm done all my chibbling. Let's go git us some chicken licking. And the two little girls brushed themselves off and carried their cans ceremoniously towards their playhouse under the spirea bushes.

* * * * * * * * * * *

That evening, after Fred and Ethelyn were in bed, Ola got out the three jars of dye she'd made up from beetroot, pokeberry juice and gentian violet. Ernest came in from washing up on the porch just as she pulled the first blue egg out with the tongs and placed it carefully on a cooling rack.

Whoa girl! You never told me the chickens'd developed blue mold. This looks pretty serious. Ola laughed and pulled one out of the pokeberry juice. Oh Lordy! he exclaimed, what do you reckon's ailin that one?

Here, she said, giving him a tablespoon and the beetroot jar. Why don't you make yourself useful? Then you can help me hide these around the barn.

Why Ola. If I didn't know you was wanting to git this done, I'd think you was gittin romantic on me here.

Don't you wish, she said, smiling. Be careful not to crack the shells. You're dropping em in there too hard. Carry em on down with the spoon and jist lay em in the dye. Oh now see? That'n's cracked.

Uh-oh. Well don't worry, it'll be the prettiest one of all. Look, the dye runs darker in them cracks and makes a sorta pattern. It's like… hmmm… like lookin through bare branches at the last apple left hangin on the tree. The way she looked at him, Ernest could tell she was more impressed than irritated, but she thought it was a stretch all the same. It's like… it's like lightning reflected in a well. No. Let's see… it's like a *spider*web across a well.

She smiled. A red spiderweb?

A spiderweb across a well at sunset. Come on—you do one.

I look at that and all I can see is a cracked egg.

He pretended to have his feelings hurt, so she said, Oh alright, you big baby. Lemme think a minute. It's like… it's like a old porcelain doorknob.

That's good. A old porcelain doorknob somebody grabbed that come in from a hog killing, he teased.

Oh you. I told you I ain't no good at games like that.

He got up and put his arms around her from behind, stroking her belly. Oh you're good, sugar plum. You're mighty good. She stopped fooling with the eggs and leaned back against him. He laughed as the baby pushed against his hand. Feels like we got us a little steer in there, a little horned critter.

He kicks the way Fred used to. If it ain't a boy it's one wild little girl, I'll say that. They stood that way for awhile, then suddenly Ola turned in his arms. Ernest, what's gonna become of us if you go to jail?

Ain't gonna happen, Oleo.

How do you know? Judge Wingate's…

Judge Wingate's full of horseshit. He and his cronies think they got ever'thing all sewed up. His brother the banker—*and* owner of the Greenberry Leaf Tobacco Barn, as Ray always says—them Wingate boys and their gang on the town council been riding high for years. Now old Arch thinks this is his ticket to even more. Thinks he's gonna impress the governor and the whole state by cracking down on us. But they showed with their little hitch-rack

stunt they don't even live in the real world. They put near ever
farmer in the county in jail, what's supposed to happen to the
economy? What's the queen bee gonna do without the worker
bees? It's all a big bluff.

I hope you're right.

I know I'm right.

Ola turned and began putting the dyed eggs into a basket. Well
come on then, let' stop fooling around and git these hid.

Cain't we fool around *while* we hide eggs?

She gave him a playful smack. Behave yourself!

Yes ma'am, he said, fishing out the cracked one, but I aim to
see that whoever finds *this* one tomorrow gits a extra helpin of pie.
It's a lucky egg.

* * * * * * * * * * *

Easter, 1920, broke bright and sunny over Wills County. The
mercury in the thermometers rose to 68 degrees, and weather-
vanes faced south and sat still. But all the good weather in the
world wasn't enough to offset the building tension in the tobac-
co-growing community.

Ola's hen and dressing dinner had been properly demolished
by the extended Oakley clan. All the women had contributed to it,
even Mrs. Oakley, who suffered badly from arthritis in her hands.
She had made special drinks: lemon phosphates for the adults,
and milk shakes for the little ones.

While the women washed the dishes, and the children went on
their Easter egg hunt in the barn, the men settled themselves with
tobacco and musical instruments in the dogtrot. Willie spiked
what was left of the lemon phosphate with moonshine, and by
the time the women were finished, the singing on the porch was
more boisterous than melodic.

As he waded crookedly into the last verse of Oh My Darlin
Clementine, Willie got a stern look from his mother. What've
y'all been up to out here?

Willie waved his empty glass with a challenging smirk. As the
other women entered the scene and took up positions, Hazel

walked on through as if she knew no one there, and out past the wagons to the front gate.

I'm goin down to see about the kids, Lora said, and left by the back steps.

It's Easter Sunday, said Mrs. Oakley. I'd have thought you could act decent on Easter Sunday... for the sake of the children at *least.*

Sorry, Miz Oakley, Ernest said sheepishly. We didn't have much.

Willie had had more than the others, however, and suddenly he dropped his glass and stood up to face his mother, towering over the old woman. You know, *I'd* have thought you'd leave off your mothering act by now. *I'd* have thought you finished with all of that after Daddy died and you up and give the goddamn *Oakley* farm to Miz Lawrence here.

The others had begun protesting this speech about halfway through it, but as Ottus and Ernest took ahold of Willie's arms to pull him off the porch, he shouted all the louder. Ola stood in the doorway, staring daggers at her brother while Earl and Joetta led Mrs. Oakley to a chair, murmuring to her in soothing tones to never mind Willie.

I jist wanna go home, she said, and then began to cry, covering her face with her gnarled hands. Since giving up this house to Ola and Ernest, home had been no more than a fleeting notion. She moved from child to child now. For the past six months or so she had been living with Willie and Joetta.

Why don't you stay here with us til the baby comes, Mama? Ola suggested quietly.

Joetta looked stung, but in the end it was decided that Mrs. Oakley would stay on with the Lawrences. Meanwhile Willie had been walked to the pond and dunked by his brothers-in-law. Then Ernest and Willie had a nap in the sketchy shade of the persimmon tree.

Ottus walked back to the barn, feeling disgusted with himself and with all human nature. He glanced up at the house and could see that Earl had gone down to Hazel, as the women sat talking on in the dogtrot. The barn doors stood open, slatted light defining the high wall at the back. There he found his young, dark-haired wife, surrounded by colored eggs and straw-strewn children. He stretched out beside her.

Anybody dead up there? Lora asked.

He shook his head with a wry smile, and they lapsed into a peaceable silence as the children continued to bring her their eggs to mind. They shouted and ran, and a few chickens scratched near the door, as Ottus lay in a kind of waking dream til the alcohol wore off.

He was all but asleep when Adell toddled triumphantly to her mother with an egg, and Lora said, Aw, it's broke. That's too bad.

Boke, Adell repeated.

Broke. BR-oke.

Boke, she said proudly, and her parents laughed.

* * * * * * * * * * *

As everybody left, Ola and her mother busied themselves inside, to avoid Willie. Mrs. Oakley had hugged little Silas and Joanie goodbye earlier, and Ernest told Joetta and Willie he'd be out the next day for his mother-in-law's things. But the gathering ended on an uncomfortable note.

After eating a light meal of left-overs, Ola and her mother bedded the children down while Ernest went out to milk the cow and see to the animals. He was kicking hay within reach of the tethered mule when a sudden voice from behind startled him into bumping his head on a low beam.

Hello there, Ernest! It was James January, his neighbor to the southeast. James's hound dog Birdie was beside him. James was a thick-set man in his mid-twenties whose thin brown hair was already receding.

Hidy, James, said Ernest, rubbing his own thickly thatched head.

James laughed heartily. Boy, you're scare-ish tonight. What's the matter? You expecting trouble?

Ernest smiled. Naw, I just wasn't expecting company. Where'd you come from? Where's your horse?

Aw I walked over. I felt like a ramble after all that food this evening, and when I seen your light down here...

Well, your timing's good. I'm about to finish up. Wanna come up to the house and set awhile? Ola's up there with her mother— she's come to stay with us til the baby's born.

James spat tobacco juice on the barn floor. That's alright. I git enough of the company of old women, what with my own mother over yonder. What I cain't seem to git much of is the company of young ones. Birdie, *git* over here! The dog came back from his jaunty round of the stable and crouched beside his master.

Ernest sat on a hay bale and gestured for James to do likewise. He pulled out his pack of cigarettes and put one in his mouth.

Man, you always buy them readymade things. Look like you're made a money.

Not hardly, said Ernest, offering one to James, but I figure, what's life for if you cain't have what you want to on some things, cause you sure as hell cain't do what you want to on most things.

James chuckled agreeably, accepting the cigarette. You been into town here lately?

Not since... oh, I reckon it was about a week ago. You?

I went in on Saturday, and goddamn it if them hitch-racks ain't all down.

Already?

Said they took em out on Friday. Kept old Moses Galbraith and his boys busy all day long. You *must've* heard about Rudy.

No, what about him? Ernest asked, frowning.

Said he went tearin into the mayor's office and give him hell about it—about them hitch-racks.

No shit? What'd old McGee say?

Aw, some line of bull about progress—you know the sorta thing. But Rudy was so het up about it that the mayor's secretary called in Deputy Meshew to restrain him.

Man. We didn't hear none of this, said Ernest. They didn't arrest him or nothing did they?

If it'd been up to McGee they might've, but Foster Meshew's about the only sensible officer of the law we got, and he smoothed it all over.

Ernest shook his head. Rudy's gonna go too far one of these days with that temper of his. Not that I blame him for being angry about the hitch-racks.

No. *Hell* no. They're asking for trouble on that.

Well next time I'm in town, I aim to tie up wherever I can. Ernest shrugged.

James's eyebrows suddenly dropped, then he laughed. You know, you might be onto something there. We could make it mighty uncomfortable for em if we'd a mind to.

Yeah. I reckon they wouldn't care to have mules across the sidewalks, but, what else can we do? Another exaggerated shrug made James guffaw.

Porch railings... Hey! I got it. How about tyin up to their cars?

Well personally, I wouldn't wanna put my animals in danger of being dragged.

Oh yeah, said James. I hadn't thought of that. Hm.

I wouldn't put it past some of em. But whatever happens, we got us a fight on our hands that ain't likely to be over with soon.

After he finished his cigarette, Ernest got up and asked again whether James would like to come up to the house with him. But he rose and declined, walking on up to the road, Birdy trotting happily ahead of him. Ernest called goodnight and went inside.

He was going to tell Ola about Rudy getting all wrought up in the mayor's office, but when he saw Mrs. Oakley sitting beside her looking drained from this afternoon's confrontation with Willie, he thought better of it.

That night, with his mother-in-law asleep in the room across the dogtrot, he pulled Ola up against him in bed and told her the story.

You know what? she said with frustration.

What?

I cain't spend the rest of my life worrying about what Rudy and Willie — and for that matter Hazel — is gonna do next. It's got poor Mama plumb wore out and I'll swear and be derned if I'm gonna let it do the same to me.

Ernest stroked her hair back at the temple and kissed her neck. Well, let's take it a step at a time. I don't see what more we can do.

Ain't no telling what they seen in that war. My cousin Jack ain't slept a full night through since he come back two years ago. Says he killed a dozen men over there, and he has to kill ever one of em all over again ever'time he falls asleep.

I know there's all of that, said Ola in a small voice. But Hazel didn't fight no war. Leastways she never joined no army.

Ernest had no answer to that and they lay in silence for awhile.

Then Ola murmured, I jist don't know what God's thinking of, stirring people up so in their minds.

Chapter Five

WELL IT FINALLY COME. At four o'clock in the morning on the Tuesday after Easter, the soldiers of the Leitchfield State Guard Machine Gun Company marched into town under Captain Williams Taylor. Righteous as a revival preacher, Judge Arch Wingate declared the town to be under martial law. The *DAILY LEAF* was full of it. Our teacher, Miss Merritt, she read it out to us, and told us how we mustn't go outside after seven at night or we'd git arrested. Virgil said he thought that sounded like fun. Boy, he caught it good.

Martial law didn't sound all that different from school to me. But I couldn't wait to see them soldiers. According to Miss Merritt, Judge Wingate'd invited the whole county to go to the court house and see for theirselves that he had *the means in place to protect witnesses.* I found out later that Ray Tibbs was also quoted in the paper, but Miss Merritt didn't read us that part. Bernard read it out to me right before supper. What he said was this: *What we are seeing is the attempt to break a populist movement of tobacco farmers. Our so-called justice system has come down on the side of the rich tobacconists who own the chute and warehouses. It will always come down on their side, not because the rich are right, but because they are the ones who run the courts in this country.*

When school let out that day ever boy who could possibly manage it hurried to the court square. Me and Delmer got trapped by the

3:45 from Memphis, which cut the town in half and stopped ever'thing for a good ten minutes. But finally the caboose went by, the feller in it waving to ever'body like we was gathered there jist to see *him* go past.

There was near as many people in town as on a Third Monday, except that it was mostly town folks. Third Monday, which was also called Mule Day for reasons anybody who'd ever saw one could figure out right away, was trade day—for country folks mostly. Today's excitement on the square, we figured, was never gonna happen again. We found Hunter in the crowd. He'd staked him out a place right across the street from the front doors of the Courthouse. He waved us over to him, and there they was! Two soldiers in full uniforms, marchin back and forth in front of the Confederate monument, where generally nothing more excitin than a game of checkers between two old men'd be takin place.

Holy crow! Hunter said, throwin a arm around each of us. Can you believe this? It's like they marched right off the newsreels over at the Dixie Theatre!

I give a whistle to show my appreciation.

Sure is something alright, Delmer said. I know we was both thinkin the same thing. How in tarnation was we supposed to be able to keep from talkin about the chute burnin with all of this goin on?

Wonder will we git to see em work one of them machine guns of theirs, Delmer mused.

Oh man, wouldn't that be amazing? Hunter jumped in. Imagine it! I bet they was ever one in the war, I said.

Course they was, Delmer said then, kindly sarcastic-like. Hell, they prob'ly got scars all over the place underneath of them uniforms.

Excuse me, private. I'd like to see your battle scars, Hunter said in this deep voice, and we all laughed and looked around to see if anybody was listenin to us, but they wasn't. In fact the crowd was thinnin out a little; people was driftin away. I reckon there's only so much walkin back and forth most folks can watch before they up and git restless.

I said I was *yearnin* to see that machine gun nest.

Machine gun nest, Hunter repeated me. Man if that don't have a ring to it....

Ever since them three words had been read out by Miss Merritt that morning ever'body'd been throwing em around, jist to feel the cold chills go up their backs. It said in the paper it was set up right inside the Courthouse doors, Hunter went on. I reckon he felt almost like he'd wrote the paper since he was a *LEAF* delivery boy.

Aw, don't go gitting worked up, Delmer advised us. We couldn't git nowhere near it.

Naw, I know, Hunter added. There's a big investigation going on in there over the chute burning.

I know that, I snapped. I tell you it was tiresome being the youngest one, not only in my family, but among my friends, too. That was one of the reasons I liked Hollis. He was my size, and six whole months younger'n me. But we'd found out at school he was home sick with the mumps. Both cheeks swole up like a chipmunk, or so they said. What a terrible time to be sick, when real live soldiers was takin over the town. I was thinkin about that when something Hunter said jerked me back to the conversation.

I can't believe you both slept through the whole thing. Man, I'd give anything to've had Night Riders right across the street from my house. I'll lay you I'd've never slept through something like that. Just think, you coulda been *witnesses*. Under oath on the witness stand. Holy crow!

I's standing there a-swarmin with my usual feelings, trying to hold back the truth about that night, but Delmer handled the situation. Shoot, bunch of little scamps like us, he said, laughin at the adult-sounding words comin out of his own mouth.

After a minute I come to and took it up. Naw, they wouldn't never listen to us. Why, we's lucky nobody's done run us off from this curbing.

Delmer reached down and picked up a broken branch from out of the street and started swattin us both with it. Go on, you kids! he said in this high, girly voice. Git on out of here, you bunch of rapscallions! You miserable scallywags!

After a minute Delmer's playful whacks begun to sting, and me and Hunter started rasslin him for the stick. We was in our own world, jist a-boilin down the sidewalk when we bumped smack into Reverend Hicks, the preacher from the First Baptist Church. Reverend Hicks was famous for being able to quote appropriate passages from scripture at the drop of a hat, and he wasn't no different that day.

Here, here, you boys! he said, glarin at us from underneath of his bushy, black eyebrows—which was the other thing he was famous for. Then, jist like that, he says, Lo, the day is coming when all the proud and all evildoers will be *stubble!* And the day that is coming will set them on *fire*, leaving them neither root, nor *branch*....

Then the preacher snatched that stick out of Delmer's hand so hard it left a welt acrost his palm that took days to go away. As he turned to leave, he said, Malachi, Chapter Three, Verse Nineteen, and then walked on down Broadway still grippin the branch. We stood there and watched him to see what he'd do with it. I don't think he even realized he still had aholt of it til he was in front of the Water n Light Buildin, cause all of a sudden he throwed it down without even breakin stride.

We turned west to walk towards Boxtown, Delmer rubbin at his hand and sayin how it didn't hurt none, it jist stung.

I said, Maybe it's what they call a flesh wound.

Yeah, he said, like he'd already thought of that. It's a flesh wound.

We walked backwards for about half a block, as long as we could still see them soldiers. When we come to 8th Street, Hunter turned for home. But even there, two blocks away from em, we could still hear them boots tramp-tramp-tramping real regular, like some sorta engine beatin away down on the court square.

* * * * * * * * * *

Jist like I'd thought, once martial law had been declared, nothing much changed. I reckon a kid lives under martial law anyhow—leastways I did. The excitement of seeing them soldiers around the courthouse soon wore off. We got used to it, the same as we done with seeing armed men around the warehouses. The tobacco market was finished for the year anyhow, so the new chute stood empty, smelling of raw lumber instead of tobacco. The biggest excitement I witnessed for awhile was Delmer knockin out Hunter's front tooth during a game of tops.

Delmer Drew was the best top spinner and marble shooter at West Ward School. He never played for funsies, only for keepsies, and since he nearly always won, the rest of us tended to play Delmer last at ringtaw.

Tops was different. Ever'body'd git in on that. We had us a top-spinnin hole dug out in the playground. We'd all put our tops down in it, and the one whose turn it was, he'd have a chance to knock the others out with his top, one at a time, til he missed. Delmer hardly ever missed.

So one recess about a week after the soldiers come, we was spinnin tops and it was Delmer's turn. He had him a red one that stood out. He was real proud of that top—took it with him ever'where. A bunch of us boys was crowded around the top spinning hole, a-shoutin an a-carryin on. Delmer had knocked out ever top but Hunter's. He took his aim and set her off jist perfect, and his top hit Hunter's so hard it flew up and busted out Hunter's new permanent tooth.

Hoo-wee, but the crack it made was awful. Hunter fell backwards and grabbed his mouth, and the blood come leakin out between his fingers. Delmer stood there starin like he'd killed him. He was white as a ghost.

Before long Hunter's mother come a-runnin—she was the fifth grade teacher at West Ward. More teachers come, and they carried him off, and Delmer had to go before the principal. Then they called me and some of the others in as witnesses. I was shakin so hard you'd have thought I done it, but I didn't like to tell on a feller, let alone Delmer.

I set there on that bench outside the principal's office for what seemed like forever. Voices from the different classrooms echoed down that big old hallway. David Cutter come out with his face all red, like he'd been cryin. Then the secretary called out my name, and my heart drummed even faster. But when they asked me what happened, I jist said it was a accident, and that's all I'd say, no matter how many times they asked me to tell em more details. It was the truth anyhow, but I wasn't namin no names.

Well, they filled in our top spinnin hole, and said they'd take and keep any tops they found at school after that. Hunter come back in a day or two with a fine new gold tooth a-flashin' in his mouth. Him and Delmer was still good friends, same as ever. And he was as sorry as the rest of us that they'd gone and shut down our top spinnin games.

* * * * * * * * * *

Course there wasn't nothin' but Investigation and Indictment talk in the newspaper and at the supper table. Judge Wingate and his 'jury of lawyers and tobacconists', as Papa called it, managed to git three witnesses to talk. Ever one of em was a Night Rider that was bribed and threatened into namin names.

I was settin out back of Uncle Berry's store on Saturday afternoon watchin Bernard make up a recipe of buggy blacking. He had me running back an forth with the ingredients as he needed em. Powdered this, and oil of that—stuff I'd never heard of before, but it was all on the shelves of the back room, labelled in Uncle Berry's big fancy writin.

I's bringin out the 'Japan Dryer' when Uncle Berry passed me on his way to have him a smoke. When I come back out, him and Bernard was settin on crates, Bernard still a-stirrin his mixture, while Uncle Berry rolled a cigarette.

How many more orders you reckon we'll git for buggy blacking now that the hitch-racks've been taken down? Bernard asked.

Uncle Berry licked the paper and sealed up his smoke. Hell, who knows? Maybe we'll be makin up automobile blacking next. He lit up and took him a good, deep draw, blowin out the smoke and settlin back against the brick wall of the buildin. Things're gittin stranger all the time.

I pulled me up a crate too from out of the pile of crates and cans and bits of lumber and such behind the store. My crate said Corned Beef Bolivia on the side, and had a blue silhouette of a bull's head. We had us a view of the backside of the freight depot. It was a altogether interestin spot, the back of Uncle Berry's grocery store.

Bert Lemon was in for groceries this mornin, and he says it's ridiculous over at the jail. Says in all his years as a jailer he ain't never seen nothin to beat it. Says even when Tom Tinker was lynched, the *crowd* was only inside the jail for a few minutes. He slays me. Guess you'd wanna have a sense of humor to be a jailer. Anyhow, he says they got the usual drunks and brawlers, plus three witnesses, and twelve Night Riders waitin for bail.

I thought the paper said thirty-eight Night Riders got indicted, Bernard puzzled.

That's right, but some of em's already paid their bail off and are free to go til their trial comes up. They're only holdin the ones ain't paid it yet.

You mean they got the witnesses in with the other Night Riders?

Oooh, wouldn't that be a party? Uncle Berry said, little puffs of smoke comin out as he laughed. Bert says they got the witnesses at one end of the hallway, and the Night Riders at the other, with ever'body else in between. Course Fred Ailsworth's in there, as usual, and he keeps runnin from one side of his cell to the other, carryin messages from the Night Riders to the witnesses. It must be comical, sure nough.

Greenberry had its share of characters in them days, and there was three colored men that was well known on the court square: Fred Ailsworth, Uncle Dave Harris, and Blackbird. If Blackbird ever had him a last name, I never heard it. He was known for his superstitious nature, Uncle Dave for his memory, and Fred Ailsworth for doin absolutely *any*thing to git people's attention. His reputation had been sealed way back when there was a chicken-eating competition. They give each contestant a live chicken to start off, an promised five dollars to the person who could kill, pluck, cook and eat it the fastest. Well he won by goin straight from the killin to the eatin. He et it *raw*, feathers and all! Now it wasn't no secret that Fred Ailsworth also drank, and he was often jailed for it, since drinkin is against the law in Wills County. So it wasn't no surprise that he'd be in there to git tangled up between the Night Riders and their witnesses.

Uncle Berry was still talkin about it. Bert was sayin these witnesses is all three young fellas that look scared half to death.

Well who could blame em? said Bernard. How can they think the Night Riders won't come after em once they're out of jail?

What are they in jail for, anyway? I asked.

For protection, knucklehead, said Bernard.

Oh, they got reason to worry alright. They jist figured the Wingates was as dangerous to cross as the Night Riders—and they're prob'ly right on that.

The Wingates? You mean Ted Wingate over at the bank, too?

Sure. Between the two of em they got ever'body at their mercy. Hell, the bank and the court both? You wanna do anything at all now—start up a bidness, borrow money on your farm, git any sorta legal per-mit—you pretty well got to work through the Wingate boys. Bert told me about this one witness—Roy Boland. He's been in the store for groceries once or twice. About twenty-one or -two with a wife and baby, and another one in the oven. Works a little farm out Harvest way. He told Bert he only joined up with the Night Riders out of fear, and then Arch Wingate told him he could make it a *whole* lot hotter for him than the Night Riders could if he didn't name them names. Bert says all three of them witnesses is young, nervous types.

Man, said Bernard, I'm awful glad Granny moved into town and Papa never took up farmin. I wouldn't wanna be caught up in this bidness.

I don't know how free any of us is, to tell you the truth.

We all set quiet for a minute. Me, I's picturin Roy Boland settin down in a jail cell with all of them Night Riders a-lookin between the bars at him. Then, all of a sudden, Uncle Berry sorta half jumped forward at me and yelled *BOO!* I about had me a heart attack then and there, and Uncle Berry and Bernard laughed fit to bust. After a minute or so I could smile about it myself.

Chapter Six

NONE OF THE WITNESSES had named Ernest Lawrence during the Grand Jury Investigation, nor had they named Willie or Rudy Oakley. Ola felt an immense relief that they had not had to take part in any of the court proceedings. Then in the third week of April, as she was getting a start on her garden, Ernest came up to her. She was setting out tomato plants, but she could tell before she looked up at him that he was excited about something.

Ola, you got any egg money put by? I need some cash money.

She didn't hesitate. It's in the coffee can on the bottom shelf of the pantry.

Thanks, honey, he said, and hurried inside.

Fred was pulling Ethelyn in his wagon, and called to his father when he came back out, Where you going, Daddy? Can I go?

Ernest patted his head, then leaned down to kiss Ethelyn on the top of hers. Not this time, horsefly.

Ola stood up and shook out her skirt. Can I ask what you need cash money for?

It's for Linton Weaver's bail. He was the last one indicted, and he refused to answer any of Wingate's questions, so he's been jailed for contempt of court. We need to raise twenty dollars to git him out.

She looked at him from under her bonnet, several unspoken questions hanging between them. He trotted over and gave her a peck on the cheek. I took out $1.50, Oleo, and I ought to be back by suppertime.

He loped around to the gate, and following him as far as the front steps, she saw him leap into a wagonload of men that waited out on the road. Cluster Higgins clicked his horse into motion and they set off southward.

He looks happy as a child at a church picnic, Ola muttered to herself. She could see Ottus plowing the field on the other side of the road. He looked up as Cluster's wagon went by, and Ola noticed that Ernest waved to him but the other men did not. Ottus lifted his chin in a salute to Ernest, but kept his hands on the plough handles. Shaking her head slowly, she turned to her gardening again.

✻ ✻ ✻ ✻ ✻ ✻ ✻ ✻ ✻ ✻ ✻

Ernest came back from town fueled to the top with camaraderie. You should've saw them people at the Courthouse when we filed in there past their soldiers and guns and laid our money down, one after another after another, til finally the clerk said, 'That'll do it.' Ray'd gone up to the counter and told em we was there to pay off Linton Weaver's bail. Apart from that not a one of us said a word. We was as formal as could be. Even when they released Linton to us, we never said a word, and nor did he. Hell, we didn't even nod. Them lawyers and reporters stood around staring at us tee-totally dumbfounded looked like.

We got back into the wagon and rode out of town. Soon's we crossed the tracks near Ray's place Cluster said, 'Three cheers for Linton!' and we commenced to whooping it up for a good quarter of a mile. We plumb forgot to let Ray off, and had to go back!

What'd Linton say? asked Ola, handing Ernest a bundle of cutlery for the table.

Well, he's mighty grateful and all of course. He said they treated him fine in jail. Ever'body's out now, by the way. Linton was the last. He said that when his turn in court come, he didn't know *what* he was gonna say right up til his name was called and he swore on the Bible. Then he said, 'When Judge Wingate asked me if I'd been part of the chute burnin, I looked up at him smilin there behind his high desk, and I could see by his eyes that smile was false. Then I brought to my mind a picture of Jesus at *His* trial—how he jist stayed quiet. I thought to myself, they're wrong and we're right. And I felt His power come into me right then and there. Old Judge Arch might jist as well've been Pontius Pilate a-settin up there. Nothing on earth could've made me name them names for him.'

Ola had stopped ladling up her squirrel stew in mid-motion. Now she continued, handing him the filled bowls. Mash that up for Ethelyn, she said. And what about the witnesses?

Ernest lifted the little girl into her high chair and set to mashing up her supper for her as he answered. Well, they've all left these parts, the best anybody can figure. The Boland place is standing almost empty, and the other two're said to be lookin pretty unlived in, too. Rumor has it Roy was going out to Oklahoma.

Ola sat down at the table, put her chin in her hand and sighed with a kind of angry resignation. Ernest looked over at her.

It's unfortunate it had to go that away, but it cain't be helped. A man's got to take the consequences of his actions.

Well, I don't much care for this side of the Association.

Me neither I can assure you.

Roy Boland's jist a kid, Ola said. Why he ain't no older'n Lora— twenty, if that.

I know it. And what's more, them soldiers looked like they oughta be in short pants theirselves—ever one of em. Yeah, I'm real sorry about Roy. If he… if they could of *all* jist handled it like Linton did….

Alright. Let's bless this food before it gits cold.

※　※　※　※　※　※　※　※　※　※　※

With the Investigation completed, the soldiers marched back to Leitchfield, and life in Wills County resumed a more natural character. Even the guards from around the warehouses were relieved of their duties. Until the June court session nothing much would happen outside of the usual routine of planting the crops and tending the animals.

As always, Ernest and Ottus worked together as much as possible. Ola had often wondered how Ottus privately viewed the Association and its ramifications. Sometimes she resented the way he felt free to let the others take the risks. At other times, such as when Roy Boland and his family were driven out, she admired his ability to stand his ground alone in this complicated business. Lora didn't seem to want to go deeply into it with her, probably because Ottus didn't say much about it. It was enough for Ola to see that her little sister was still crazy in love with Ottus, and happy. For her part, Lora could have the dark, silent type. Ola was glad she had a husband who talked to her, and who *laughed*.

Now Ernest went out and milked Bertha for her, morning and evening. As often as not when he came back in for breakfast he'd find all three of them in bed, singing and telling stories. If the weather didn't permit him to go into the fields, he'd throw off his clothes and climb back in with them, saying, Shove over there and let your poor old Daddy into his own bed! The children would giggle and pretend to try to keep him out so that he would wrestle with them.

There was so much rain in the early summer of 1920 that they had quite a few such mornings. But somehow they got the crops into the field, and completed the daily rounds of chores.

On the last Saturday of April the Lawrences walked down the muddy road to the Drews for their weekly singalong. The sky hung low and obscured the sunset. Fred waded through all the puddles in his bare feet, Ethclyn playing follow the leader right behind him. As they neared the house they saw that it was crowded with people, and Berry Rule's wagon sat in the driveway. Hardin and Nell had borrowed it, and had brought along Ottus's mother and her three youngest children, as well as Granny Rule.

Hardin nodded to them from behind his big bass fiddle; he and Ottus were already tuning up, so Ernest hurried to join them. The women were in the kitchen popping corn and slicing Nell's pound cake. Bridget Ruth had brought some old magazines, and she and the girls sat on Ottus and Lora's bed cutting out paper dolls. Fred ran out to join Pat, Delmer and Harry who were playing tag.

Ruth said, I'm feelin so good tonight I might jist have to dance me a jig.

Nell laughed. You do it, Ruth, and I'll join you.

Me too, said Granny, and they all hooted.

Alrighty Mama, I'm gonna hold you to it, said Ruth. What about you girls?

Well now, Ola said, patting her belly, I ain't liable to be dancin no jigs for awhile. I reckon I'll have to be content with singing while y'all do the fancy footwork.

They warmed up with Turkey in the Straw and some of their usual tunes, Shady Grove and Sweet Willie. When Ruth requested a jig, Ernest said, Oooh I learned a *beaut* off of Tom Duffy over at the Livery Stable last week. It's a old Irish tune called Burning the Mortgage. Any of y'all know it?

They said they'd catch on, so Ernest lit into it, gathering a trail of guitar and bass notes behind him as he went. The second time through, the four women got up and began dancing in the way that'd been passed down by the generation that came from Ireland during the famine migration. The children came in to see what all the whooping and thundering was about, and stood shyly smiling to see mothers, aunts and grandmother—and especially their great-grandmother—behaving in such a way as this. Ola clapped the time, and the younger children whirled and jumped around in an exuberant, makeshift dance of their own.

Later in the evening, while the men took a smoking break, Ruth Drew told the story of how Ottus came by his guitar. He was about ten years old. We had us a gathering like this one here. The other kids was restless and fidgety, but I could tell by the way Ottus set so still that he had something on his mind. He didn't never ask me and Perry for a guitar—I reckon he knew he wouldn't git one that away. What he done was ask for a corner of the back pasture over here to plant in tobacco for hisself. Perry was that pleased to see a boy so enterprising that he granted it to him, on the condition he'd work it only after his regular chores was done.

So Ottus fenced it off and cultivated it—took as good care of it as any crop of tobacco ever *was* took care of. The others used to call it his 'baby farm'. But he didn't take no notice of nobody, jist worked away. It was only after four years of him taking his share of the crop to market with his daddy's load that we seen what he'd been intending all along. He went into Paducah with Perry one Saturday, and he come back home toting that guitar there.

I had figured he was up to something, but I never guessed what til I seen that instrument, then it all fell into place. From that day on, he spent any spare time he had a-strummin at it and foolin with it. He learnt to raise chords first, then fragments of songs, and finally whole tunes.

Just then the three men came back inside, and Ruth grew silent, knowing how much Ottus would hate being centered out.

Why don't y'all play After the Ball is Over? Granny suggested, to cover the slight embarrassment. I always think that'n's mighty pretty. What's more I know most of the words to it, which I cain't say about too many songs.

* * * * * * * * * * *

While the men had sat out on the back porch chewing or smoking according to the preference of each, Hardin had been telling them about the violin his brother Berry had recently acquired.

It's the damndest thing how he got it. A hobo riding the rails through here along about Christmas, swapped it for a load of grocerics. Now ain't that a helluva trade?

Depends on the violin, said Ernest. You reckon it's any good?

Aw you oughta see it. That tramp made a poor bargain, if you ask me. It's the prettiest little thing. Got mother of pearl flowers inlaid on the tail piece *and* on the bow. Got a label inside that you can read through them f-holes that says it's a genuine copy of a Stradivarius.... All three men laughed at this rather questionable boast. But wait, now. I'm gittin to the most important part. I got it restrung and tuned, and I'm here to tell you, listening to the music outa that little fiddle is like hearing the angels cry.

Ottus couldn't wipe the smile off his face to hear Hardin's melo-dramatic metaphor, but Ernest was interested. Well, ever'body knows Berry Rule cain't play a washboard. What's he planning to do—sell it?

Here Hardin smiled with self-satisfaction. Nawsir. He told that hobo he'd hold onto to it for a year, and he told *me*—his little brother—that if he don't never come back, I can have it.

What if he does come back? asked Ottus.

If he does, he can work for awhile and Berry'll let him have his fiddle back, jist like he said. But he ain't never coming back.

How come you're so sure? asked Ernest.

Berry said he looked brutalated from drink. Besides, you wouldn't never give up that little violin unless you knew you was dying. I reckon that poor fella knew he was going to meet his Maker in a ash heap or somewhere before too awful long.

They lapsed into silence for a moment, then Ottus made a faint noise. Hmmmm…. It was a barely audible, one-note lament, but Ernest decided he'd better get Ottus back inside before he be-came too morose to play any more party music.

It was late by the time everyone left. Hardin gave the Lawrences a ride over to their place in Berry's wagon, since both Ethelyn and Fred had fallen asleep, and Ola looked like she could fall asleep her-self. While he was dropping them off, Lora got her two down to bed.

The others gathered on the front porch, waiting. Nell sat in a porch chair with Pat on her lap, their heads together in the spill of lamplight from the window.

You know, Nell, said Granny suddenly, it's come to me what color y'all's hair is.

They all looked at her quizzically. They both got red hair, Granny, said Bridget Ruth, beginning to think her grandmother was losing her sight or her wits or both.

Folks calls it red, but it ain't red like a apple or a rooster comb, now is it?

Bridget Ruth had to admit it wasn't.

"Which jist goes to show you ought to not believe ever'thing folks says. Look at it. That hair is exactly the color of strong iced tea. They laughed and murmured assent.

Just then Hardin returned, and they all started towards the wagon. Nell shepherded a very sleepy Pat out to where Ottus hoisted him up, followed by Debry and Fairy. But when he turned to help Delmer up as well, his little brother shook his head no, to indicate that he was no baby in need of help to get into a wagon. Ottus boxed him lightly in the arm, Okay, Delmer, you're in charge of makin sure nobody falls out on the way home, you hear?

Delmer nodded.

Ruth was standing near the apple tree she'd planted beside the driveway years before. Ottus walked over to her. Well, Ma, ain't we takin' care of the place to suit you?

She turned around and smiled. Place looks real nice, Ottus. I was jist lookin at how the rain's washed the blossoms near offa this poor tree this year. Such a pity. I always loved it when this tree was in bloom.

Do you think that'll affect it's bearing? he asked.

Naw, she said, drawing the word out flat for emphasis. You mark my words, it'll put out the best June apples in the county, jist like it always does. And you mind that I git some of em, too.

We will, Ma, he said, putting an arm around her shoulders and walking her towards the wagon. We always do.

He helped her up, then he and Lora waved and watched the wagon roll away down the road and disappear into the darkness.

Chapter Seven

WITH MAY COME THE END OF SCHOOL, which was always a highlight of the year for me. Me and Hollis and Debry was finished with the third grade, and Hunter and Delmer was already done with the sixth! We run out of that school buildin like it was on fire, and on into the sunshine. First thing Delmer done was hollow out our top spinning hole again. But we didn't hang around there for long. Them shady streets was a-callin to us to be away from the place of our imprisonment. Summertime stood before me like a golden cup, and I could fill it up with whatever I wanted to.

The Saturday night after school let out there was a barn dance Papa was gonna play for, so that was the first excitement. It was gonna be held in the Enterprise Barn, and Mama and Bridget Ruth and even Bernard was on the decorating committee. Me, I was helping to fetch and carry.

We'd been at it for hours when Mama and Papa got there after work. Papa and Pony Hayden set up the bandstand. Mama and Bridget Ruth worked on the doorway decorations. They was tying blossoming branches onto these archway frameworks that folks'd have to walk under no matter which door they come in through.

Berry'd give Bernard the afternoon off from the grocery. He was carryin tables and chairs around with some of his friends, Cecil Halcomb and Daniel Erwin and them. They was one of em was called

Dunn. I never did know his Christian name. Ever'body called him
Bout.

A dance always caused us big excitement cause Papa played for
em. And when Papa was excited we was all excited. It was contagious
on him. After they got the bandstand all set up, I watched em tune
up and practice. Papa could play pretty near anything it seemed like
to me. Sometimes he played piano for the Dixie Theater—that was
before the talkies come in. But I seen him play a trumpet and a squee-
zebox, and of course anything with strings. But mostly for dances he
played his bass fiddle.

I loved to watch him and the others play. Papa was *good*. He'd take
and hold that big old instrument up to him like he loved it more'n
anything in the world. He told me once that he'd first saw Mama
while he was playing a dance. What caught his eye, he said, was that
her hair was the same color as the wood of his bass fiddle. Then he
winked an said, She's shaped somethin like it, too.

We went home and et supper and changed our clothes. When we
come back they had lamps lit all around, and before you could say
Jack Spratt that big barn had begun to fill up. Tobacco barn dances
was the most democratic gatherin's in Wills County. Except for the
color bar, which held firm, all the usual walls folks put up come down
at a barn dance. Didn't matter what your religion was, cause even
if you didn't believe in dancing you'd come to visit; didn't matter
whether you lived in town or out in the county; didn't even *much*
matter whether you was rich or poor, from Boxtown or the Bon
Ton—which was what they called the high quality neighborhood.
Ever'body come together inside the music Papa and them made, and
lemme tell you it was *fun*.

For a kid it wasn't dancin, but ever'thing else that made it fun.
When the crowds had come through them blossomy arches, and
the music commenced to cranking up, Tom Duffy announced that
they's gonna play Fly Around, My Pretty Little Miss. That's when
I made for the long refreshment table to see what all was on it. Well,
I was disappointed, cause they wasn't but a big bowl of punch at
either end. Bridget Ruth come up to me in her Sunday dress and
hissed at me to stop hangin around there or people'd think I didn't
git no supper.

They don't put the cookies and stuff out til later. Go do something. Like what?

Like ask some girl to dance. What do you think this is anyway?

I crossed my arms over my Sunday shirt and backed away from her. If she thought I was gonna ask a girl to dance, why she had her another think coming. After that I lost her in the crowd and got to studying who was there. Ever'body it looked like, except for Hollis. Miz Schultz never come to the dances. I seen Sheriff Jones and Deputy Meshew sorta visitin with people and keepin a eye out at the same time. Mayor McGee was there with his wife. So was Judge Wingate and his, but his brother the banker never showed hisself at public gatherings, so it wasn't no surprise he wasn't there. Papa always said, if Arch Wingate had the whole town in his pocket, Ted Wingate had Arch in *his*—whatever that meant. But I could see how it'd be hard to dance with Judge Arch in your pocket.

I didn't see none of my friends about, though I did see Bernard dancing with Caroline Tressider. He looked all sorta glassy eyed and serious, and she was talkin his ear off. Then Hunter's folks waltzed by, and Miz Hancock smiled at me so I high-tailed it to the back end of the place, in case she'd wanna talk about school. Papa and them was playin Likes Likker Better'n Me and I was near the north door when it occurred to me if Mr. and Miz Hancock was here, Hunter must be too. But I'd done landed in a place that caught my interest, because they was a knot of veterans outside the door, and they was spikin each other's punch with moonshine. Willie and Rudy Oakley was amongst em, and James January, so naturally I begun to look for Ottus or Ernest, but they wasn't there.

James January, with his hair all slicked back, was saying, Did y'all see Minnie Skaggs? Hoo-wee, but she's lookin as pretty as a Third Monday mule tonight.

The others laughed, and Rudy said, You shoulda let me cut that hair of yours last week, if you got eyes for Minnie Skaggs.

Then Willie said, Aw what do you want with the mayor's secretary anyhow? You'd never git no peace. You'd be on a direct line to the courthouse ever minute of your life.

Which might not be so bad, if you was wantin information, said Cluster Higgins. But if it's privacy you's after, well....

I'd been hopin to hear about the war, and it didn't look like things was gonna go that direction. So I turned around to move off, and jist when I heard Willie Oakley say something about the June court session, I bumped right into Sheriff Jones.

Scuze me, son, he said, walkin around me towards the moonshine gang. Then Hunter called out to me from inside the barn, and I missed what was said. By the time I looked back, the Sheriff was holding up his cup of punch for a little hit of the moonshine. So much for the excitin arrest I was thinkin I might git to see.

Hunter and me walked around the edge of the Enterprise, looking over the crowd. Then we seen Ray Tibbs talking to Mayor McGee. Thinking maybe *this*'d be promisin, we sidled up behind em to eavesdrop.

Now listen, Ray, the mayor was sayin, soundin nervous. I know what you're gonna say and I agree with you.

Oh you do, do you?

Course I do. Folks that drive buggies needs hitch-racks. I know that. But I got to do what the majority on council votes for, and I... we... we jist felt like this was a safety issue.

Uh huh, I see. And y'all felt ever'body'd be safer if the animals remain unhitched while they're in town?

Jist then Judge Wingate come up, and slapped Ray Tibbs so hard on the back it caused his tobacco plug to splatter to the floor. RAY, my old friend, he says in a loud voice. Oh, pardon me, did I do that? Why, good lord. Clyde, go find Noble Duffy to clean up this mess. He's about somewhere. Out back around the trashcans I expect.

The mayor left like he was in a all-fired hurry, and Judge Wingate said, Noble. Ain't it funny the names Negroes give their children? I'd offer you another plug, but I don't chew. Like a cigar?

Ray Tibbs was mopping his chin with his handkerchief. No tha...

What's that you say, Ray?

I said...

You know, it's so loud at these dances, I jist can't seem to hear you. Arch, you're...

Say what? said the judge, cuppin his hand behind one ear.

Suddenly Ray Tibbs up and walked away, and the judge stood there laughin to hisself.

I was kindly disgusted with Ray Tibbs for not sluggin the judge there and then. You'd have never guessed he's the head of the dadgum Night Riders if you hadn't've knowed it.

Papa and them was playing The Missouri Waltz and me and Hunter decided to go outside an git us up a game of hide-n-seek. I knowed Delmer was about somewhere, and maybe some of the other fellers too if we was to go lookin. Seemed like a dance wasn't what it was cracked up to be without you didn't have your friends with you.

* * * * * * * * * *

I'd plumb forgot about the Night Riders, except in nightmares ever once in a while. Me and my friends was busy playin and runnin and doin like boys does in the summertime. Then one night at supper Papa said, Court opens on Monday, and the first item on the docket is the chute burnin.

I know it, said Mama. That's all anybody at work can talk about.

Granny was having supper with us that night, and she got kindly tetchy all of a sudden. It wasn't nothin she *said*, jist a feeling she give off around her. She folded up a griddle cake and dipped it in the butter on her plate and didn't say a word. But it was one of them talking kinda silences.

Finally Bridget Ruth said, right out of the blue, Mama, I wanna git my hair bobbed like all the other girls.

Well you've thought she'd said she wanted to jump off the Courthouse spire. This big old argument started and I thought Mama'd never put out the peach cobbler I knowed she had for dessert. Ever'body ended up a nervous wreck, and I put it all down to that derned chute burnin business. Ever'time it come up, seemed like people got as jumpy as a long tailed cat in a room full of rockin chairs. Bridget Ruth went to bed cryin and Bernard went off to see what the Erwins was doing and wouldn't take me with him. Granny went home in a pout, and Papa said he was gonna go to practice over at Pony's. Which left me and Mama alone on the porch swing.

I was settin there beside her trying to figure out how to git away somewhere myself, when she pulled me over against her and said, Aw Pat, sometimes I git so blue I don't know what to do.

It shocked me. I didn't know what to say. Mama never talked that away. She was always so busy, maybe she didn't have time to git into blue moods, though I had knowed her to git into black ones ever once in a while. I leaned against her, and waited to see what else she'd say. That was the night she told me about her sister, Bridgie.

I had always knowed Mama had a younger sister named Bridgie that Bridget Ruth was partly named for. And I knowed that she had died way back yonder before any of us was born. But I hadn't never heard the story of her dying til that night in the swing after Bridget Ruth said she wanted to bob her long hair all off and ever'body pitched such a hissy fit. I don't know why Mama started talkin about it then when she never had before, but I remember as clear as anything that's when she told me the story.

Mama was born in a family of six girls, and one boy. He was the youngest one, our Uncle Tom, and I reckon he come too late to be of much help with the farm. When her older sisters started leavin home to git married and such, Mama and Bridgie moved to Greenberry to work at the Woolen Mills. They boarded at Miz Hayden's Boarding House like a lot of country people that moved into town done. This was about 1901 or 2. Mama was comin up to eighteen and Bridgie sixteen when they moved to town.

Well, it wasn't long before Bridgie was took with a coughin sickness that wouldn't go away, and sure enough it turned out to be the consumption. They shared a room there at Miz Hayden's, and Mama looked after Bridgie the best she could, but Bridgie wouldn't hear of goin back to the farm or quittin work. She wanted to be a town girl.

Mama said it got worse and worse. Said sometimes when Bridgie got to coughin real bad, a image'd come into her mind: I'd think a my Mama washin out thin, cotton baby dresses like I used to see her do when Florence and Tom was babies—a-rubbin em so hard up and down that washboard til I was sure she'd wear holes in em. Oh it was awful to listen to her coughin, especially in the night. Bridgie was real thin to start out with, and there ain't nothin can be done about TB.

This went on til 1904, when, a few days before Christmas, they was walkin to work and Mama suddenly noticed when they got outside in the light, that Bridgie was lookin sicker'n usual: She'd coughed a lot in the night, that wasn't nothing new. But this day she was glassy-eyed, and white as a sheet with these red circles on her cheeks. Looked like a puff of wind'd blow her over. I stripped off a glove and put a hand to her forehead, and she was burnin up. So I said, 'Girl, you cain't go in there today. You ought to stay in bed.'

She wouldn't hear it, and jist kept on a-walkin. I tried to make her go back. I said, 'Bridgie, I mean it. You go back and git in the bed. I'll tell em you're sick.' I stopped walkin, but she jist went on real slow without me. So I caught up to her and said again for her to go back. Then she says to me, 'I got to go in, Nell. Don't you see? If I turn and go back to that bed, I'll never git up again.'

Mama was tough as a stump. She didn't cry easy, but I could hear her voice goin all quavery-like, and it kindly got to me. But wasn't no goin back. Her story had aholt of both of us.

She kept on tellin it: Bridgie worked a sewing machine in the room right beside of the weave room. From my loom I could see her if I leaned around a little. Well she coughed and coughed all that morning, and I seen that Mr. Sanders noticed. He walks up and down the whole length of the Woolen Mills ever'day, jist to keep a eye on the workers. Doesn't do nothin hisself far as I can see, cept smoke them cigars of his. But leastways we always git a warnin when he's coming cause of the smell of his smoke. So I was a-worryin about Bridgie's health, but also about her gittin in trouble with the company. I reckoned gittin fired'd finish her for sure.

We wasn't supposed to go to the outhouse if we could help it. They kept a eye out for anybody that wasn't at their station. So when I smelt that cigar smoke again late that mornin, I looked over and seen Bridgie was gone. I left my loom and went over there and asked Nancy Willett, who worked beside of her, where she'd went, and Nancy yelled over the racket, 'Outhouse!' I asked how long ago, and she said, 'I don't know—maybe twenty minutes?'

Well, I begun to run down them long aisles of machinery. I had to git to the far door that led to the yard with the outhouse. When I got there I found Bridgie, leanin up against the side of it without her coat on. She was coughin up blood. It was all down the front of her dress. 'Oh Bridgie,' I said, and I took her in my arms. We jist sorta sank down together, for she'd gone limp as a rag. People started runnin towards us, but there wasn't no help for it. She died right there in my arms. She wasn't but seventeen years old.

Mama went silent. Nothin more to tell. We wasn't much for huggin and carryin on that away in our family. We was shy of expressin our love out in the open, but that didn't mean it wasn't there. It was jist understood, like the air you breathed. I's still leanin up against Mama with my arms around her waist, so I jist patted her like. We couldn't neither one of us say nothing right then. But I didn't think no more that night about how I could git away and play. I set on with Mama til bedtime, jist a-listenin to the crickets, as she kept on a-swingin us back and forth.

* * * * * * * * * * *

As it got closer to the June court term, people got more snappish. They put out more calls for witnesses, since it looked like the three they'd got the last time wasn't plannin to come back. Far as I know, they ain't none of em *ever* come back, to this day. It was all over the papers that the governor was offering a $500 reward for anybody who'd tell the Grand Jury what they knowed about that night. It was all the talk. But Papa said any $500 bills that got handed out was only good for startin over someplace far away.

The Sunday before court was due to open again, Granny called me over next door to help her snap beans. Really it was jist to keep her company, but she'd never say it like that. We was standin there at her table a-workin, and I was askin her about the signs. I loved when Granny told about them. She said you was supposed to do ever'thing by the signs. Why, she'd say, we built us that house out yonder according to the signs.

I'd heard all of this a hundred times I reckon, but I wanted to hear it again. What do you mean, you built it by the signs?

Jist what I said! She looked at me like she hadn't never seen a boy so slow in all her born days. We waited for a full moon night, and then we took and laid out the foundations for the house according to how them shadders was a-layin right at midnight. Then we come back the next day and set to buildin it. And you can ask Ernest and Ola if that house ain't as sturdy now as the day it uz built.

But how did you and Grandaddy know how to read that moonlight?

My Pappy helped us. He knowed all about the signs. But it's all there in your almanack, as plain as day.

Sometimes I couldn't feature what Granny said, but other times I actually couldn't understand her, cause she had a powerful country accent. Mountain-Irish, Papa called it. She'd be tellin me about the old days, about how her folks come from over the mountains in 'Kaliney' in covered wagons, tyin logs to the back to slow em down after they come over the top of one. I thought Kaliney must be a town in Ireland, since I knowed they's born in the old country. It was Uncle Berry told me years later she was saying Carolina. Or another time she'd hold her nose and say, Shoo-wee! Git that outa here, it's smells like carn! Turns out there's a word for rotten meat—carrion—an that's what she meant, but I didn't know that word then, and wasn't nobody could tell me what 'carn' was for the longest time. And she said 'arn' for iron, and I don't know what all. So my mind was always a-workin when I was around Granny—which I reckon, now, was a good thing.

Anyhow, there I was listenin to her tell about the old days, and say how young folks had done forgot that they oughta talk to their old folks, and nobody bothered with the likes a her no more. Well, I wasn't saying much cause I didn't like to contradict her, but I was confused, cause if me standin there all day askin her about the signs wasn't young folks talkin to old folks I didn't stand much chance of recognizin it. Then all of a sudden, she changed direction on me. All of a sudden she asks me, says, Pat, you ever check y'all's mailbox?

Granny was a constant surprise. I said, Well, I would if there's ever anything in it for me, but since it ain't nothin to do with me I leave it be.

I thought it a odd question, but she didn't say no more. Jist nodded her head, and went on cuttin up liver with her old green-handled scissors. Usually she was a big talker, but after that she got in a mood, like ever'body else had been in lately, and it was up to me to make all the conversation. I got tellin her how I wanted a dog but Mama'd said no. I thought maybe she'd take up for me like she sometimes done, but she jist grunted-like and didn't seem like she was even listenin. Wasn't like her.

When I finished them beans I asked if I could go, and she said, sorta huffy-like, Why-ever not? It ain't like I'm holding you prisoner here, Pat.

That wasn't exactly no parting blessin, but I left anyhow. First thing I done was to go over to our porch and look in the mailbox. It was empty as a pocket. Course it was a Sunday.

So then I went over to Hollis's. His mama said we couldn't go off nowhere, so me and him was settin around listenin to her complain about the blue laws that made ever'thing stay closed on Sundays. She'd run outa cornmeal which she was needin to make supper, so she sent us to the neighbors to borry some. While we was walkin back we seen Judge an Miz Wingate out for a Sunday walk. Their two boys was ridin shiny new bicycles. We all arrived at the Schultz's front walk at about the same time, ready to say hello and pass on. But Miz Schultz snatched up two-year-old Albert, who'd been whinin all afternoon with the earache and drivin us all crazy. She packed him out to the walk and said, Scuze me, Judge, but I wonder if I could ask you a favor?

Judge Wingate was a big man, and he swept off his bowler hat and almost hit his wife with his cane makin a showy bow to Miz Schultz. Why certainly, ma'am. What can I do for you?

While the grown-ups talked, his boys, who I judged to be about four and six, pulled their bicycles to the curbing and looked us up and down like we's for sale at a cattle auction or something. I reckon they was scared we might ask to ride them bicycles.

Albert was a-whinin and squirmin on his mama's shoulder, and she said, Little Albert here has the earache, and I chew, and none of my neighbors smokes. I, I wonder... if you wouldn't mind...

The judge didn't wait for her to finish. Certainly, he said again, and stepped forward real ceremonious-like. Albert cried and tried to shrink away from the big man with the loud voice who was loomin up over him. But Miz Schultz held him firm, and Judge Wingate took a deep draw on his cigar, then cuppin them huge hands of his around that little-bitty ear, he leaned down and blew smoke right into it.

* * * * * * * * * *

By the time Third Monday rolled around in June, the court term had closed and ever'body could breathe easy again. The chute burnin cases was 'continued' due to lack of witnesses. That meant they'd push em along til next time, which wouldn't come til November.

There was a big crowd around the court square like always on Mule Day, and a lot of voices raised in storytellin and deal makin. Me and Delmer made our way through the tangle of wagons and mules, delighted that it was summer. Durin the schoolyear we'd git over to it soon's we could, but it'd already be thinnin out by late afternoon, and we'd have missed most of it. We wasn't no fools. We understood the education that was to be had around the court square on a Third Monday.

Mules was the primary item of business, and boy did they ever primp em up if they was for sale. They'd curry em, and trick em out in bows and decorative harnesses—anything to make em look as young and desirable as each particular animal could possibly look. But it wasn't only mules that got swapped and sold. All manner of para- phernalia changed hands, from livestock to pocket knives. Women'd trade household goods. A bolt of muslin for a sausage grinder. You'd see crates of crazy lookin ducks or chickens like you hadn't never saw before, with a clump of feathers stickin right up out of their heads or something. One time we seen a little-bitty goat, no bigger'n a cat—I ain't foolin. I never *will* forget the way that little white goat stood on a upturned bucket in that wagon bed and looked around.

But this day me and Delmer was on the look-out for pups, which they was always plenty of. We found us a crate of Springer Spaniels that fed our appetite for meltin eyes and waggedy tails to a tee, and we crouched down beside of em ready to stay there all day long. Next thing, jist as I'd reached through the slats to touch the silky coat of the one I'd decided I'd take—if I was takin one—this old man come up behind us and said, They're for sale if you want 'em, boys.

Me and Delmer looked at one another.

I ain't askin much for em, and they make fine huntin dogs. He wasn't gonna leave us alone, we could see that. So, without a word, we got up at the same time and went on, them pups jist a-whinin for us to take em with us. My heart was about broke, but Delmer took me by the elbow and said, Don't keep lookin. Ain't no use in even askin—you know that. C'mon, let's go find Blackbird.

Like Granny, Blackbird was good for a hour of stories about his superstitions, advisin you on practical ways to avoid all manner of misfortune. But also he never went nowhere without his matched terriers, Pete an Repeat. And he didn't mind lettin you pet em as long as you wanted to.

So we set off amongst all them overalls and print dresses to look for Blackbird. But that day he wasn't nowhere to be found. So we had to be content with Uncle Dave, who was settin in his usual place near the corner of 6th and Broadway on the court square curbing.

Uncle Dave Harris didn't have no dogs, but he had him a cane that I thought for years was magic. It was a remembering cane. He was said by ever'body to be about a hundred years old, though didn't nobody know for sure, not even Uncle Dave hisself. He told me once that he was born into slavery, and never did know his own family, not even his mama. Her name was Oretta, and she died when he was a baby. He was raised by other slaves, and never did hear who his daddy was.

Whether it was to make up for the loss of his own history, or whether he jist had a gift, I couldn't say, but Uncle Dave carried the entire history of the county in his head. He was blind when I knowed him, though you'd never guess it to look at him, and he had notches cut in his cane that he used to keep track of the generations as he counted em back. He's jist like Jesus at the well, Uncle Berry used to say. He'll tell you ever'thing you ever done.

Now that was a exaggeration. He couldn't do that, cause there was a lot of things I done that Uncle Dave never told me about. But what he could do was tell you your family line back to whenever your people come into this country, even if that was right back to Indian days.

The first time Hollis met him, he wanted to know if he was some sorta fortune teller. Uncle Dave laughed, stroked his long, kinky beard, and said, Nawsuh. I am a prophet sho'nough, but I don't know what's comin, jes what's passed. I am a prophet of the past. I remembah what eva'body else fo'gets.

That Mule Day he's settin jist behind where Rudy Oakley was workin his barberin business out of the black satchel-bag he carried with him ever'where he went. Most people was aware that, down amongst them scissors and combs, Rudy had him a revolver. I'd never heard of him takin it out, but the fact that it was there give him a air of mystery. While he didn't enjoy quite as strong a reputation for edginess as his brother Willie, still and all, folks didn't generally push him too far. Today he had Cluster Higgins in the rickety, press-back chair he brung along for his barberin.

Uncle Dave was jist listenin to their talk, I reckon. We come up and set down on either side of him and told him who we was, since he couldn't see us. He smiled like he was pleased to have our company.

Pretty crowded today, Delmer remarked to the old man.

Yes, it sho is. Noisy too.

George Adams's daddy says you's descended from African story-tellers, is the reason you can member things so good, I said. He's the janitor over at the high school, and the *principal* done told him that.

Uncle Dave give a soft chuckle. Well, that may be so. All I know is I's lived in Wills County all of my life, and the good Lord done bless-ed me with a powerful memory. I cain't explain it no bettah than that.

Do me, Uncle Dave, said Delmer. You ain't done me in a long time.

Alright, honey, I'll do you.

I hadn't never heard a man call a boy honey—specially Delmer—and it took me a generation or two to git control of a fit a laughing that was wantin to take me, but I done it.

You's Delmer Drew. Son a Perry. Son a Winston. With each name, he moved his thumb down a notch. There was five notches in all, though most folks didn't require but only three.

Do me now, I said, but Delmer cut in. Wait, he ain't done Mama's line yet.

Alright, Uncle Dave said, real pleasant-like. Yo mother is Ruth, daughter of Nancy an Padrig. Now, which a *them* shall I follah?

Foller Granny Rule. You done Padrig last time.

Now I was gittin in a stew, cause Delmer was doin my own line like it didn't have nothin to do with me.

Alright then. She is Nancy, daughter of Barbara and Billy Bean.

I was jist about to insist on my turn and have him do Mama—since her line wasn't nothin to do with Delmer—when Blackbird come down the walk with his two terriers. Before we could call out to him, Blackbird seen that Rudy had cut the left side of Cluster Higgins's thin, collar-length, salt and pepper hair off to his earlobe, and was preparing to finish the job.

Wait, Mr. Oakley! Stop! cried Blackbird. Mr. Higgins, you oughtn't to be gettin yo hair cut jes right now!

You git the hell outa here, Blackbird, Rudy said, settin his jaw.

What you tryin to do—ruin my bidness?

Nawsa, Mr. Oakley. I's only tryin save Mr. Higgins from a bad headache. It's goin against the signs to get your hair cut in this here quarter of the moon. It'll leave you with a headache for a whole month, and...

Here was the signs again. But it was clear they didn't tickle Rudy like they done me.

He pointed them scissors at Blackbird and said, I done told you once—git on outa here fore I have to cut off more'n your hair!

Blackbird took off without another word, and me and Delmer didn't never come acrost him again that day. Cluster sat like he's frozen in the chair as Rudy carried on snippin. When James January sauntered up and asked what Blackbird was so worked up about, Cluster started to explain, but he didn't git no futher'n a couple of words before Rudy slapped him upside the head and said, You never mind explainin that nonsense. Seemed like Cluster Higgins was destined to git him a headache one way or another that day.

It also looked like our exploration of the generations was over, cause about that time, Uncle Dave rose to his feet, and said, Boys, let's take us a little walk over to the cornah opposite this one. We figured he jist didn't like bein near that powder keg, so we obliged him, and helped him maneuver through the wagons and all. Turns out he was wantin us to guide him to the northeast corner of 6th and Broadway, where city hall stood. But there wasn't no place for him to sit over there, and we was wonderin what he's up to, or if he was jist senile, when he says, Would y'all like me to tell you somethin *nobody* else remembahs?

Sure, Uncle Dave, we said, raisin our eyebrows at each other.

Y'all know what stood on this cornah ninety years ago when I's a boy?

A log cabin! I guessed.

Uncle Dave shook his head, both hands on his cane. His chin was raised, and he was standin straight as a monument.

A tcepee! said Delmer.

He shook his head again. Then, frownin a little over them old vacant eyes, like he could see it before him, he said, A auction block. A old wooden auction block. This heah's is the very spot where I's sold to the Harris family.

Chapter Eight

LORA WAS ON HER KNEES in the garden when she heard Adell scream. She scrambled up from among the flowering stalks and climbing vines, wiping her hands on her apron as she ran. Harry turned to look when she burst into the front room where she'd left them napping an hour before.

It ain't nothing only Midnight, Mama, he said.

Lora looked over and saw that the cat had caught a mouse and was playing with it under the kitchen table. Harry stood observing Midnight's strange pleasure as he repeatedly let the mouse move away, then clamped a paw over its tail and took the dazed creature into his mouth to shake it and toss it up in the air.

Lora sat down on Adell's bed and took the child into her arms, where she gave in to her revulsion and shuddered against her mother. Adell honey, I know it ain't nice to watch, Lora said, rocking the tiny girl back and forth. Harry, open up the back door an git him on outa the house, will you?

Adell buried her face in her mother's warm neck as the soothing voice continued. I know how you feel, sugar lump. I never could stand to watch no cat with a mouse either. But it's a necessary part of life. That's why we *feed* Midnight—so he'll kill the mice around here for us. He's only doing his job.

Harry was holding the back door open and calling the cat's name, but Midnight ignored him, fully absorbed in his torturing. Finally Harry propped the door open with one of his father's barn boots, and walked over to the table to get Midnight. He had often carried the big cat around, but now when he reached down Midnight delivered a long tight unearthly yowl. Still holding the mouse down with one paw, he stared flat-eared up at Harry with such naked hatred the boy fled to his mother's side.

Come on, y'all, said Lora, moving towards the front door with the two children. We'll go outside ourselves til he gits done. Y'all can help me in the garden.

She left the back door propped open on purpose, hoping Midnight would take his catch outside. But when she went back in later that afternoon, though the cat was gone, the slain mouse lay in the middle of the floor and the house was full of flies. Lora took an old newspaper, scooped up the tiny body and threw it behind the outhouse. Then, calling to Harry to get the fly swatter from its nail beside the door and get busy, she put a dab of honey into a small bowl and set it on the window sill.

She was about to begin making supper when Ernest came riding into the yard on Ottus's bicycle, which he'd borrowed for exactly this purpose. Lora! he called, jumping off and running inside. Lora, it's time! She went into labor at about noon, but this'n's comin on faster'n the others did. Miz Oakley says to come if you can. You take the bicycle—I'll bring Harry and Adell in the baby carriage.

She left her apron on and started towards the front steps, where the fallen bicycle lay. Does Ottus know?

We's workin in the six-acre field when Miz Oakley come for me, so he'll know where you're at.

Ain't you sent for Dr. Barton?

Your mama says she can handle it and save us the fee.

Lora jumped on the bicycle and pedalled hard, raising a trail of dust along the dirt road. It didn't take five minutes, but she was still too late. Fred and Ethelyn were playing on the swing Ernest had put up for them in the white oak tree beside the fence. Lora called ahead to Fred to open the gate, then rode on past them, not taking time to prop the bicycle, but throwing it down beside the steps as Ernest had. Tearing into the bedroom she found her mother washing a big hairless boy in Ola's red and white enamel dish pan.

Why land sakes alive, you mean to say it's already all over? she panted.

The fun part is, said Mrs. Oakley without smiling. But I'm powerful glad to see you walk in here with them good, strong hands of yours, Lora hon. It's all I can do to keep aholt of this big boy with my crooked old claws. Here, you take over with him, and I'll see about the afterbirth.

Ola lay in the bed with her knees up, calm and seemingly oblivious to the gore on the sheets. She smiled when Lora brought the baby over wrapped in a receiving blanket, and handed him down to her.

Looks like you got you another pretty, blond boy.

Ola beamed as she took him, then she inhaled his newborn scent and put him to her breast. Lora went around to the foot of the bed to help their mother clean up all the blood and water.

Throw that wash water out, and bring me that basin, said Mrs. Oakley.

Lora did so, and shortly her mother gave her back the enamel pan with the afterbirth in it, saying, You best bury this, fore it don't draw no wolves.

✻ ✻ ✻ ✻ ✻ ✻ ✻ ✻ ✻ ✻ ✻

When baby Ralph was two weeks old, Mrs. Oakley left the Lawrences to go down to Tennessee, where her two eldest sons lived. They and their wives farmed about five miles from each other, and she would be gone for a year or so, spending six months with each. Ernest, Fred and Ethelyn took her into Greenberry to catch the train to Union City.

Before she climbed up onto the wagon bench, Ola gave her mother a long hug. Mama, she said, you know you can stay on here permanent if you want to.

Mrs. Oakley smiled, but didn't look her daughter in the eye. Now you know what ever'body'd say if I's to choose one over the rest. They'd say I was playing favorites. Naw, I'll be a gypsy all the rest of my days I reckon.

You come to us anytime you want to, I don't care what nobody says—you hear me, Mama?

I hear you, my girl, she called, still not looking directly at Ola, who stood with her feet planted a little apart, in defiance of the tears she was fighting.

Well, we'll miss you. We'll send you down your part of the crop money like always.

After waving them off, Ola fed the chickens, gathered and candled the eggs. The heat was oppressive, though it was only ten o'clock. It made the baby fussy. After nursing him to sleep, she lay him in the buggy with an old window screen over it to keep off flies and mosquitoes, and parked him just inside the barn where it was a little cooler. Then, tying on her bonnet, she went to whitewash the side of the chicken house she had started last May, and never gotten back to.

From where she worked she could see that the cows had waded into the pond and were standing there like statues, as if willing away the heat. Must be nice to have your only job be keeping yourself cool, thought Ola wryly. From there her mind wandered to how hot it would be for her mother on the train. She and Ernest had discussed the offer to have her live permanently with them, knowing what an adjustment that would require for everyone. In some ways it probably was best that she rotate among her children, Ola thought, though it was no insurance against the charge of favoritism.

A sudden gust of wind carried the scent of the tobacco blossoms over from the six-acre field. It was a sickeningly sweet smell, like gum drops, and served only to remind Ola that they must soon top the tobacco. She dipped her brush to run it over the last grey planks, and found that several chicken feathers had blown onto the freshly painted wall with the gust. She picked them out, sighing, as more feathers and dust eddied up. Finally she finished, and wiping her damp forehead with her apron, strode through drifts of truculent chickens towards the barn. She was more than ready to go and sit in the dogtrot for awhile.

The barn was only slightly cooler than the chicken yard, a sort of warming oven, heavy with the aroma of hay and dung. Briefly, Ola hung above the screened buggy and looked at her newborn son. He lay flushed with the heat, sleeping deeply, almost doubling in size as she looked, like a loaf of uncooked yeast bread left to rise under a dishcloth. Carefully, so carefully, she turned the buggy and rolled him across the tufted grass of the yard to the house.

* * * * * * * * * * *

Worming began at dawn. It was still dark out when Ola started cooking breakfast. Ottus and Lora came whispering to the door, and put Harry and Adell into the bed she and Ernest had gotten out of. Then, as soon as they'd eaten, Lora and the men went out to the six-acre field to get started.

Ola was washing up the dishes when Ralph began to fuss. She went over and lifted him from his crib. You want your breakfast, too, don't you, hon? she whispered, not wishing to wake the other children. Grabbing her snuff box from the mantel, she carried Ralph out onto the back porch. From there she could watch the sun come up over the pond. The dew-rinsed air was mild and fresh, not yet oppressive. She unbuttoned her dress and the baby fastened himself onto her left nipple, sucking with the rhythm of a little machine. She was soon working the snuff in her mouth to a similar rhythm, and thinking how lucky she was to miss the worming this year.

August was a crippling month for tobacco farmers. They had just finished topping the plants, breaking off the sticky flowers til their arms ached and their fingers were glued together. But no one who'd ever worked tobacco would be likely to argue the fact that worming was the most odious part of the labor involved. In the thirty days between topping and cutting, the plants had to be suckered and wormed. The process was repulsive, monotonous and exhausting, but it had to be done.

Ola was in the fields by the time she was five years old. Impossible as it seemed to her, it would soon be time for Fred to begin helping. He would go with the others next year, sitting in the damp grass until there was enough light to see them by; then he would crawl on his hands and knees, picking the soft, green worms off the undersides of the broad leaves. They were as thick as a man's finger, and you killed them by squashing their heads between your thumb and forefinger. Squeamishness could not be tolerated; there was no time for it.

Ever worm-eaten leaf costs me money, Ola's father used to say. Y'all mash ever one of them devils—it's us against them. Kill em! You kill em jist as fast as you can.

Some people threw them on the ground after killing them, but Ola insisted they be stowed in a pail or sack and saved for chicken feed. Her disgust at mashing the worm heads hadn't outlived her first summer in the patch. She looked upon the memory of her childish revulsion the way you might look upon an antique turned up in the garden, or passed down from your grandparents—something that has no use anymore, and is merely cute. But still and all, she never had been able to *bite* the heads off and spit them into the dirt, the way her brothers did. And she knew only too well, the physical miseries of worming, the near despair of turning at the end of a long row only to have to start back up the next.

When Brother Walker talked of Adam and Eve being cast out of Eden to work by the sweat of their brows, the congregation of the Hickory Methodist Church did not drift off to daydreaming. They listened to every word because this was about them, pure and simple.

Ain't no doubting the Bible, Ralph, Ola said quietly as she shifted him to the other breast. You'll know that by the time you're five years old. He took hold of her finger with the concentrated grip of one working to survive. And you're gonna need them strong hands of yours. The good Lord done give you what you need, didn't He, precious? He give you good *strong* hands.

She went on murmuring to him, as the sun blazed up over the pond like a flaming sword in the hands of an angel, barring the way back to Paradise.

※　※　※　※　※　※　※　※　※　※　※

In the golden days of September, when town children ambled back to school in the slight loosening of the summer heat, farm families bent to the heavy task of cutting tobacco. In 1920, because the planting of the 'hundred day crop' had been delayed by rain in May and early June, it was late September before cutting time came.

Ernest had hired a crew of black people to work alongside himself and Ottus. Lucas and Hilda Flowers and their four eldest children had worked for him before. They had recommended Alma June Smith and her three sons. Alma June's husband had run off with another woman and she'd come up from Tennessee to live with relatives in Hickory Grove. Her sons were young and thin for the work, but Ernest had masked his dismay when he saw them. Ottus, however, didn't edit himself once he and Ernest were alone.

Fine bunch of hands you hired there, Ernest, he commented, as they watched them start down the rows with froes and tobacco knives. Hell, them last two cain't be much older'n Harry and Fred.

They're older'n they look. They're eleven-year-old twins—Silas and Cletus.

Twins. Well, I reckon that explains their size. They never even got a meal to theirselves when they's inside of their mother.

Ernest gave Ottus a look. True enough, Ottus, but hell, long as we got you standing around here all morning passing opinions, I don't see what we got to worry about. They grinned an unspoken challenge at one another, and Ernest followed the workers into the field, calling out to them as he walked, All right now. This morning we'll all work at splitting the plants. Jist take care you split em right down the middle. I don't want em falling off them sticks and settin fire to my barn.

Ernest kept an especially close eye on the twins, showing them how to slice straight down the middle of the stalk. They proved attentive and eager to please, stopping only when Fred and Harry pulled the red wagon to the edge of the field at mid-morning with water jugs and glasses.

By the time Fred came back and hollered to them that dinner was ready, enough of the tobacco plants lay wilting on the mounds to make Ernest and Ottus both feel better about their cutting crew. Now the Smith twins dropped their knives and, with a hand to the small of their backs, scampered after Fred to where the women waited beside the barn doors.

It was cool inside, and the workers' stomachs growled as they caught the delicious smells rising from the crowded table. Ola and Lora had worked all morning, too. There was hog jowl and green beans, corn on the cob, sliced tomatoes, cucumbers in vinegar, black-eyed peas, field peas, turnip greens, cornbread, and fried apple pies. Jugs of buttermilk, sweet milk and water stood on a second table alongside plates, glasses and cutlery.

Fifteen-year-old Lily Flowers had felt the eyes of the oldest Smith boy on her all morning and she was plagued with self-consciousness, as well as hunger and fatigue. At the end of the table she turned and collided with Cletus, dropping her full plate upside-down onto the dirt floor of the barn. Putting her tobacco-stained hands over her face, Lily broke down and sobbed. Alma June pulled Cletus to her by one ear and began scolding the daylights out of him, but Ola led Lily back to the end of the line, saying, It don't matter. Don't matter one bit now. You jist come and start over.

The girl's mother picked up the plate and was about to start clearing away the mess, when Lora said, Jist leave it be, Hilda. Between the cat and the chickens, it'll all git cleaned up directly. That's the beauty of eatin out in the barn.

They sat on an assortment of chairs and logs carried in for the purpose, the two black families on one side of the circle, and the two white families on the other. Except for Ethelyn.

The Drew and Lawrence children had been fed early and put down for naps with Bethy to watch over them. But knowing Fred was up and helping, Ethelyn had been unable to sleep. As soon as Adell and the others dropped off, Bethy made a trip to the outhouse. Ethelyn took the opportunity to slide out of bed and go down to the dark fire barn to watch the excitement.

The three-year-old had arrived at the barn door just as Lily dropped her plate. Her heart wrung with sympathy, Ethelyn walked behind the other diners as soon as they were seated and stood beside Lily. Lily looked at Ethelyn, her red eyes taking in the earnest little face under the short, boyish haircut. She patted the log beside her and Ethelyn sat down, scooting gradually closer and closer to Lily.

Ain't you hongry? Lily asked.

Ethelyn shook her head. Then, to Lily's surprise, the little girl reached up and began stroking her arm. Lily accepted the gesture, smiling down at her. But Ethelyn soon became absorbed in studying the contrast between her salmon pink hand against Lily's dark brown arm. Lily laid down her fork on the near-empty plate and turned her hand over. Her palm was pink, like Ethelyn's, with a yellow stain from her morning's work. They smiled at each other and Ethelyn turned up her palms.

Soon the other diners began to stir, and Lily took back her hand in order to finish up her dinner. When Ernest led the way back into the field, she tied her straw hat on and grabbed a fried pie to eat as she walked. Wading into the field, feeling full and happy again, Lily turned back once to wave at the tiny figure beside the barn door. A few rows over she heard Mrs. Smith hiss, Richard! Watch where you a-walkin.

So, his name was Richard.

* * * * * * * * * * *

The next morning, as soon as the cutting crew climbed down from Ernest's wagon, he drove it over to the barn where Ottus was waiting. Together they lifted the metal scaffold and a pile of tobacco sticks onto the wagon bed and drove it back to the field.

The Flowers and Smith families were already back at the splitting. Ernest went to direct that part of the work, sending the younger members of the crew back to Ottus. The latter group carried their tobacco knives to where the work had begun the day before. There they cut off the plants at the base and brought them to the wagon, where they carefully hung nine wilted plants upside-down on each tobacco stick.

At noon they fell to their barn feast, sticky with sweat and tobacco gum. After the meal Ola and Lora helped in the field, so that the men and the oldest boys of the crew could begin housing the crop.

Ernest took pride in working the collar beam, the highest tier in the tall barn. Ottus was right below him in the middle level of 'rooms', as the frame sections were called. Lucas Flowers and his eldest son, Hiram, took each golden-leafed pole from the boys on the wagon and handed it up to Ottus, who passed it on up to Ernest. One foot balanced on each beam, and dripping with sweat in the heat that pooled under the barn roof, Ernest accepted the first pole from Ottus and settled it carefully into place under the dark peak. The reverse of mining gold, he thought, reaching for the next one.

※ ※ ※ ※ ※ ※ ※ ※ ※ ※ ※

In the fall of that year Ottus Drew was plagued with fire dreams. Licking tongues of flame kept him writhing on the feather ticking several nights a week it seemed. Such nightmares were common among tobacco farmers in this season as they housed their crops in the tall, narrow barns for dark firing. Ottus had experienced the occasional fire dream every October since taking over his parents' farm, but this year they were a scourge. He blamed the chute burning trouble. The November court term was looming, and all the tensions were heating up, right on cue.

In his recurring dream, the tobacco barn would catch fire. Like predators, the flames would run across the field to the house where he and Lora and the children were sleeping. With that peculiar logic dreams have, the flames would seep into the house, leaving the walls intact. They would cover the floor like long grass, framing the doorway between the two bedrooms. As he and Lora sat up in bed, the flames would jump up onto the edges of the quilt. Lora would scream out the children's names while he tried to beat back the flames with his pillow.

After one such dream he came awake with a groan and bounded to the west window. From there, as the dream flames receded and his eyes adjusted, he could see the tall, grey barn still standing, curing smoke pluming out steadily from beneath its eaves.

Ever'thing okay, Ottus? Lora asked sleepily from her pillow. Three months pregnant with their third child, she didn't wake easily these days.

Yeah, it looks alright from here, but I'll go take a look inside, jist to be sure.

Every year several barns in the county burned down. A poorly split hand of tobacco falling into the fire, or tails from the lowest tier poles igniting could take your whole year's crop. So could Night Riders. It paid to check often.

Pulling on his work clothes, Ottus padded quietly past Harry and Adell's beds in the front room, their deep, peaceful breathing snagging at his heart with an intensity that still sometimes surprised him. Making his way through the dark room, Ottus went out across the back porch and into the small hours, stopping to draw a bucket of water from the cistern. The fragrance of curing smoke soothed his lungs as he crossed the field. Tonight the sky hung overhead like a winter's supply of dark meat up in the smokehouse rafters, all salted down with stars.

At the barn he removed the brace planks, unaware in his concentration, of the door squeaking on its hinges. Through a small opening he beheld the banked hickory fires below the hanging tobacco. The hands of tobacco looked like inverted tongues of flame themselves, yellow-green at first, but as the season progressed, gradually changing to a proper reddish-brown, as if adopting the character of the curing fires below.

Satisfied that the only fire was the good fire he himself had set, Ottus dashed the bucketful of water at the walls to build up some humidity, and re-sealed the barn. Then, smelling as rich as the bowl of a pipe, he returned to Lora, who drew him to her to breathe in the scent of hickory smoke in his hair. Her sleepy feast of curing smoke soon turned into love-making.

Ottus? she said afterwards.

Hmmm?

How'd your daddy handle not being in the Association?

He pulled back from her and studied her eyes. She never questioned him about this. Maybe she was worrying about bringing another baby into the powder keg atmosphere created by the chute burning cases. He sighed and turned over onto his back. Daddy jist used to say he'd never join. He'd say, 'Anybody raises a hickory stick to my back in the name of brotherhood or anything else, can go straight to hell.'

Did Night Riders ever visit y'all?

Naw. But he always said if they ever did they'd have a helluva fight on their hands.

She said no more and when Ottus had dozed off into a dreamless sleep, Lora rose with the red sun and went out to see to the animals.

Chapter Nine

NOVEMBER'S WHEN THEY STRIP TOBACCO, settin around a brazier tearin the leaves off and classin em out. Then they twist em into 'hands' and set em aside til market time. I didn't never see too much of that when I was a kid cause it come during school time. But you knowed it was going on from the general talk, like in Uncle Berry's store when the farmers'd come in for their supplies. Them words 'strippin tobacca' would hang in the middle of ever conversation seemed like.

And that year, when I was coming up to my ninth birthday, they's all talking about the November court term coming up, too. Them court terms—in April, June and November—they was always inconvenient for farmers. But, come to think of it, most times is inconvenient for tobacco farmers. Leastways they was back in them days. Dark tobacco is a fourteen-month crop, Papa used to say, and it don't never give you a break, cept down in your back.

Anyhow, ol Judge Wingate took up his threats and warnings in the *LEAF* again, and Ray Tibbs took up his counter arguments, and ever'body got all testy jist like last time. It was the same ol thing that whole year and on into the next, cause in November—jist like in April and June—the cases against the Night Riders was continued. The paper said the farmers was too busy, but ever'body knowed it was cause them witnesses wasn't coming back, and without witnesses there wasn't no case. It jist wasn't worth it to *no*body to volunteer to git on that witness stand, seemed like.

All of this was in the air, like I said, but as for me, all I was thinkin about was the cap gun I wanted for my birthday. A cap gun and a roll of caps—that was the shape of true happiness for me at that time. As November come toward its close, and the sky turned all grey and silver-like most of the time and the leaves was blowed away, why that was my time of year.

My birthday, the 28th, fell on a Sunday in 1920. So on Saturday when I was havin my weekly bath I was allowed the privilege of goin first. Usually, what with being not only the youngest, but most likely the dirtiest too, I'd go after Bridget Ruth and Bernard had already went. We'd pack our water in, pail by pail, from the pump in the yard, and heat it up on the stove. Then we'd fill us up a washtub there in the kitchen and scrub ourselves raw. Oh Lord, how I hated them Saturday baths.

I finished up and brushed my teeth over the kitchen sink while Bernard took *his* washtub punishment. I'd been droppin all sorts of hints about the cap gun for days, but when I climbed into bed I hollered out my prayers for Mama and Papa's benefit jist in case: God bless us all and make us be good, and *please God git me a cap gun for my birthday* amen. If Mama and Papa heard me, they never let on.

The next day, after Mass, we had my favorite wintertime dinner, pork chops and mashed potatoes. Then Mama carried in a cocoanut cake with nine flamin candles on it and they all sung me Happy Birthday. Granny was there and she laughed while Bernard and Bridget Ruth give me my nine birthday spanks. Then come my presents. Granny'd knit me a sweater, and Bridget Ruth and Bernard give me a bag of marbles. Papa, he winked and went off to his and Mama's bedroom to git me their present. I was expectin he'd have that cap gun in his pocket, but he come back in there carryin a little set of drums.

Here you go, Pat, he said. I thought it was time you was brought into the orchestra.

See Ruth took piano lessons, and Bernard was tryin to learn the trumpet. Them drums pleased me, sure enough, and I set to makin a good deal of racket right off. It run all the women out soon as they'd finished their cake, and Papa and me and Bernard had us a musical afternoon. I soon got the hang of them drums, and I played on em for years. Don't know what ever become of em in the end. I hate how that happens. Even things you once treasured can jist disappear off into thin air when you ain't payin much attention to em no more.

* * * * * * * * * *

Even with them drums though, I was a little bit blue over the cap gun, but I didn't let on none. And come Christmas morning there it was in my stockin along with some hickory nuts and peppermints and a roll of caps. We had us a big turkey and dressin dinner. Some of Mama's sisters come, and Granny Touhey. Then Granny Rule and Uncle Berry and more relations than you could shake a stick at got stuffed into that little house, so me and Delmer struck out across town to see what Hollis and Hunter was doin.

We showed one another our pocket knives and cowboy hats and whatnot. Ever'body was well pleased with Christmas. We was about to take Dixie out for a ride when Miz Wingate's colored maid, Magnolia, come along the sidewalk usherin a crowd of children towards the judge's house on the corner.

Come on, y'all, she called to us. Don't y'all wanna come see what Santy brung Archie and David for Christmas?

Sure, we'll come, Magnolia, Hunter answered for all of us. We looked at him like he was crazy and he whispered, They do this every year. You don't have to stay long and they serve you boxed candy and eggnog.

So we trailed along at the back, and that was the one and only time I was ever inside of one of them Wingate's houses. Archie and David was younger'n us, and they had em settin on chairs beside of the biggest Christmas tree I'd ever saw. It was odd. It was like they was on display theirselves. All around their feet was toys like you'd see in Carter's window. There was a rockin horse, I member, and a train set and... I don't know what all. What got to me the most was a brand new ball and bat. Now I'd have give anything for a ball and bat. We always used us a broomstick and a rock, but we was pretty good even with them. I couldn't help but think what we could do if we had us a real baseball and bat.

The Lenihan girls that lived two doors down from Hunter was sayin how nice it all was and makin polite talk with Miz Wingate. The rest of us jist stared. It made our presents look pretty thin, which I reckon was the point of the exercise. Magnolia come around with candy, jist like Hunter'd said, and told us to take one, and make sure it was the first one we touched. I wondered at them bein so stingy with us when they was so rich—we'd a never thought of tellin a guest how much they was allowed to take. But then, Mama always did say them Wingates was as tight as the bark on a tree. When the box come past Delmer, he said he'd accidentally touched two, and me and Hollis couldn't look at one another afterwards. Bein in Judge Wingate's house was sorta like bein in church; you jist knew you wasn't supposed to laugh.

The judge and his wife set on this big fancy pink couch with fringe a-hangin off of it. He was smokin a cigar and lookin us all over in a way you wouldn't exactly call friendly. Amused, that'd be the word for it. They had em this big old mirror over the mantel, and it was in a gold frame that had cherubs flying right directly at each other across the top of it. Their windows was covered up with so much cloth you jist knowed they had a lot to hide. Ever'where you looked was fancy ceilin lamps and such. It was a house to make you set up real straight.

I looked at Archie and David a-settin there while we drank us a glass of eggnog, and I actually felt sorry for em. But when I caught Archie's eye and smiled, he give me a look of pure-out murder. I knocked back my eggnog and turned to git on outa there. We all done like that at about the same time. The Lenihan girls said goodbye, and we all said thank you like we's brung up to do.

Jist as us kids was leavin out a automobile pulled up to the front curbing and John Lewis, Ted Wingate's colored chauffeur jumped out. He run around and opened up the door and the other Miz Wingate—Miss Maddie—scooched out, a-tuggin at her skirt. The Lenihan girls and me bein Catholic, we knowed her from church, so we all said hello to her. She smiled at us, and said, Merry Christmas, children.

Behind her come her banker husband. He was wearin a sorta cowboy hat like the one Hollis'd got from Santy, but Mr. Wingate's wasn't made of straw. It was the real thing. It was white. He didn't go to St.

Joseph's—didn't go to no church at all as far as anybody knowed. And he didn't even look at us, jist cast his cold, blue eyes forward like we wasn't there. He put out his elbow, and his wife took aholt of it and they went inside, with John Lewis right behind em, packin in a stack more of presents.

Mama didn't care for them Wingates. She said they'd got above theirselves, and to show she wasn't fooled by em she always called em by their first names. Now there wasn't many done that. When she'd pass the banker Wingate on the street and he'd tip his hat and say, Mornin', Nell, she'd always say, Hello, Ted, jist like he was anybody else. And she done the same way with Judge Arch. But she had knowed em way back yonder, when they was jist like the rest of us.

Mama said their daddy had run him a grocery down on East Broadway. When he died, their mama married a tobacco farmer and Arch and the others had gone to live out in the country. But Ted, who was the oldest of the four Wingate boys, he'd refused to go live with his step-daddy. He'd stayed on in their little old house—Mama said it was jist like ours, a boxed house. But livin alone there and doin odd jobs around town—mostly housepaintin—he'd taken to the drink. Mama said it wasn't til Arch become a lawyer and started makin something of hisself, that Ted sort of woke up. And she said it wasn't til he married Miss Maddie, whose daddy run the bank out at Harvest, that he done any good at all.

Aw, Mama was death on them Wingates. Ever'body knowed Ted Wingate's habit of knockin on his office window when somebody he wanted to talk to—wanted to bully, as Papa put it—walked down 7th Street past the bank corner. Most folks'd stop whatever they was doin and answer his summons. Not Mama. He thinks he owns this whole town, Mama'd say. Well he don't own me. If I had to go all the way to Louisville to do my bidness, I'd do it jist to keep it out of Ted Wingate's hands. They's crooks, the pair of em. They got the money and the law all tied up, or so they think. But they ain't never gittin no power over me, so long as I got a word to say about it.

Papa'd rare his head back and laugh when she talked that away. You tell 'em, Nell, he'd say. Then he'd look at me and Bernard and say, You boys remember your Mama when you come to marry. Git yourself a strong woman. It can only do you good. Then he'd jist beam at her

Wagons lined up for market at the Tobacco Chute, North 13th Street, circa 1918

Ruth Drew, mother of Ottus & Delmer, circa 1928

Granny Rule, nee Nancy Bean, on her front porch, circa 1924

Uncle Dave Harris before he went blind, circa 1910

Courthouse in spring

Mule Day on the Court Square, early 1920s

Berry Rule's Grocery, 1924, Uncle Berry on the right

View from the Court Square after the hitch-racks were removed, 1921

School photo, 1922: Pat Rule 2nd row, 2nd from left; Fairy Drew front row, far right

Front row, L to R: Ralph Lawrence, Adell Drew; Back row, L to R: unknown boy, Harry Drew, Fred Lawrence, 1921, not long before the massacre

L to R: Harry Drew, unknown boy, Adell Drew, Ralph, Ethelyn & Fred Lawrence, 1921

Ernest Lawrence

Ola Lawrence

Lora Drew

Ottus Drew

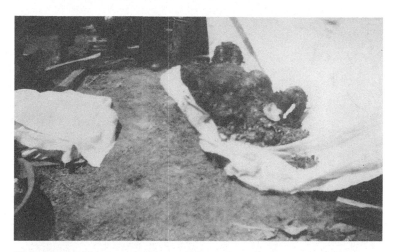

The remains

Remains sorted into a wicker casket & an iron bowl

Crowd around the remains, June 26th, 1921

Fred Ailsworth
at work on the
ash heap, June
26th, 1921

The Carter hearse

*The scene of the massacre, June 27th, 1921; Funeral of the Drews &
Lawrences, June 27th, 1921*

and she'd blush and say, I mean what I say, Hardin Rule. And he'd give his head a little approvin shake and say, I know you do. That's what I like.

* * * * * * * * * * *

In January, the tobacco market was in full swing over at the new chute. Prices started out low, but the paper said the higher quality "weed" would soon start to show, and with it higher prices. Then things begun to look bad again as stories of Night Rider raids in the counties to the east of us started showin up in the newspaper. There must've been a dozen or more reports of barn burnings and beatings dosed out to farmers who wasn't in the Association.

I was over at Granny's after school one day helpin her crack nuts for her divinity candy when she seen Ottus. He was settin up on his wagon bench all wrapped in a blanket, nearly to the chute in the long line of wagons waitin their turn. It's cold as a froe out there, Pat. Run acrost and ask him does he fancy something to eat, or a cup of coffee, will you hon?

I done like she said, and he give me a faint sorta smile, like I'd brung him back from a daydream. Lora done packed me some food, but tell Granny I'd sure appreciate a cup of hot coffee.

Once she got it ready, she had me to carry it on over to him, with some of the candy she'd made for herself. She didn't take hers with nuts on account of she didn't have no teeth, but she always made up some with nuts in it for us while she was at it.

Don't spill that coffee, and tell him I'll be along in a minute to have a visit.

I done all that, and went back to my nut crackin. She'd gone to the outhouse, and when she got back she took and carried the *LEAF* out to him. I went over to the door and I seen her climb up onto the wagon bench and set down beside of him. He shared his blanket with her, and I could see the two of em huddled there a-lookin at the paper. They was talkin real serious when the bell give out with a clang, and Ottus urged the mule forward another wagon length.

I got on back to crackin them nuts, and the next time I went to check on things Ottus was walkin towards Granny's front porch

with the newspaper in his hand. Granny was holdin the reins for
him. I barely had time to git back in the kitchen fore he's in the door,
a-stampin and a-shiverin. He come on in the kitchen with his empty
cup and the newspaper, and hovered over the stove a minute to git
hisself warm, throwin the *LEAF* down on the table.

He looked over at me, no smile this time. He was frownin kindly
cross-like, so I kept on at them nuts, jist a-pickin em outa their shells
like it was real important to me. We didn't pass a single word. After
a minute, he went out the back door to visit the outhouse, and it was
like a storm had passed over. I liked Ottus well enough, but he could
be scary sometimes with that silence of his.

By and by Granny come back in. She'd quietened up some herself,
where she'd been tee-totally normal before she went outside. The
thought of leavin come to me, but I couldn't decide whether my goin
right then would rile her or please her. It was easy to see something
had happened between her and Ottus.

Granny, I said finally, scoopin nuts off the edge of the table into the
little crockery bowl she had half full already, what's the matter?

Well, I'll tell you, Pat. She said it real short, so I knowed there
wasn't no gittin out for awhile. Then she commenced to tellin me she
was worried about Ottus.

He's jist like his daddy was. Ain't nobody never gonna tell him
what to do, and I wasn't even tryin to. All I said was I thought he
ought to know what was happenin. I ain't tellin no tales outa school
here nor nothing. A man's gotta do what he thinks is right, but... I
mean, this bidness of the Association, it ain't no easy matter.... I cain't
help but worry about him.

She cut herself off there and looked at me. I jist looked back at
her. Like usual, all I wanted was to wander off and play awhile before
supper. But I didn't like to see Granny upset.

Then she smiled all of a sudden. Turned out it was at something
from way back yonder. You know, Pat, little babies is all darlin. But,
long about the time they commence talkin, that's when you start to see
something of their character—apart from all the other little babies, I
mean. The first time I knew the sorta person Ottus was gonna be he
was about three year old I reckon, and we was readin that little picture
book of Bible stories. He ups and says, 'Which one's God?' I pointed

out Jesus, and he looked up at me to see was I crazy, and he said, 'In that *dress?*' Well I fell to laughin and he caught my chin in his little old hands and said, 'Don't laugh, Granny. I know God don't wear no dress.' Then he slid down off of my lap and went off to be by hisself. Now that's jist who Ottus is. He showed it early and I reckon he'll never change.

She chuckled again at the memory and never did say no more, but she'd worked herself around to a better mood, so I reckoned I could go on off and play. But I was still in the dark about the whole incident. Seemed to me like I couldn't never git a straight answer from nobody. It was always parables and stories, and you was left to sort through it the best way you could.

* * * * * * * * * *

That was the winter I seen my first hog killin. What with Uncle Berry runnin the best meat market in town, we never had no need of goin in on one. But that year Ottus invited Delmer and Bernard and me out to help with one on a Saturday in late January. It's my opinion that Uncle Berry put him up to it so Bernard could learn more of the butcherin trade. Besides they was always tryin to keep us town boys from becomin too soft and forgittin our roots. Shoot, I was game. I thought it sounded like fun. Now that right there'll tell you how little I knowed.

To begin with it was cold. They had to pick a cold day for hog killin without the meat wouldn't spoil while you was workin it. Lora give us a extry sweater and pair of socks each, sayin, It's colder'n a widow's toes out there. We walked into the field behind the stable where Ottus kept his hogs, our breath in the first light a day hangin in front each one of us like a white cloud. Ernest and Willie and Rudy was already there. Willie was stampin and a-huggin on hisself, and he says, Hoo-whee, it's colder'n a witch's tit out here. I didn't know no more about witches' tits than I did about widows' toes, but I reckoned anybody that said it was cold as *anything* was right about it.

We'd carried some equipment—knives and pans, tubs and shovels—down from the house and set em at the base of this big old oak tree like we's told to. First we hollered us out a big hole in the ground near that same tree. Then we built us a fire down in the hole, and I worked like a squirrel gatherin kindling for it. Then the men pulled a big metal thing—looked like a boat sorta—took and pulled it right over that firehole. They called it a vat and they had me and Delmer and Bernard to fill that thing up with water, which took us a right smart. It got to boilin pretty good after while. By and by I warmed up, what with the fire and all the haulin too.

I heard em sayin' it was time, and discussin which pig. They was about eight or ten of em in the field, a-rootin in the pile of corn and apples Lora kept goin for em. She'd told us how she had been specially good to em for the weeks leadin up to hog killin cause it makes the meat taste better, so leastways I reckon they died happy. Anyway, Ottus took his rifle up there and aimed at the one he's wantin from about twenty feet off. He shot her right between the eyes and she dropped down dead as a doornail. The rest of them pigs didn't even seem to notice or care, except for a little sideways shuffle when the gun went off. It was odd.

I wasn't expectin em to shoot the pig with a gun. Papa had told us that *his* daddy used to pole-axe 'em with a mallet, and that he thought that was kinder'n the way some farmers strung em up live and slit their throat. Anyway the second that pig dropped, they sprung into action. The men took and carried her over near the vat, and Ottus told Bernard to git him a pan to collect the blood. Me and Delmer walked over closer so we could see. Ernest and Willie rolled her over, while Ottus dipped a long butcher knife into the boilin water. Then Ernest held up her head, saying, Okay now Bernard, put your pan under her neck. Naw, right under it. Yeah, that away.

Next thing, Ottus sticks his knife into her neck real deep, and the blood jist come a-spurtin out and filled up that pan in no time. The smell of it kindly got to me so I stepped back some. I seen Bernard was looking a little peaked too, but wasn't nothin he could do cept hold that pan in place.

Anything you kill you got to let em bleed clean, Ernest explained. If you don't you're gonna taste it in your meat. And you watch Ottus when he guts a hog. If them intestines bust when you're slicin her open, you'll taint your meat and lose it. You watch how careful he opens her up.

I reckon Ernest jist meant to teach us about it all but I was really wishin he'd stop talkin about guts and such, when they decided she was done bleedin out.

Delmer, you carry that blood on up to the house for Lora to cook.

I know Uncle Berry'd a laughed if he coulda saw my face right then. Delmer jist whispered, Blood sausage, to me and took and carried the pan of blood on outa there, trying not to spill none. He'd saw hog killins before of course and wasn't quite so 'delicate' as me and Bernard. That's what Willie took to callin us all day. Y'all are too delicate for this part, ain't you? and comments such as that. Finally, Ottus told him to shut up about us or leave. Things got kindly tense for awhile, but Willie didn't leave—I reckon he allowed as how he'd be needing their help for his own hog killin.

After the bleedin they took and heaved her into that boilin water. Once she was steamed real good, they run em a hook through each of her hocks, then they took ropes and hauled her up into the tree. We all took turns scrapin her with butcher knives. That part wasn't so bad. The boilin makes the hair fall out pretty easy. I didn't mind shavin on the smooth parts. Delmer, he hunkered down and set to work on the head, talkin barber talk while he shaved her jaws and her nostrils and all around her ears. It was kindly comical, if you didn't dwell on it too much.

You take special care of them ears, Rudy told him. That's my favorite part. Ain't nothin like pig's ears when they's boilt right.

While we was doin this, they went and shot em another one and started the process all over again. While the second one bled and boilt, Ottus brung his butcher knife over to the first one, and set to guttin her. We got a tin tub under her, and he placed the knife jist so at the top end of the belly, which was real soft, and he cut into her. He sliced along, openin up a seam, and holdin the guts back from the knife as they tried to tumble out. When he had her opened up all the way down, he let them guts go, and they slopped out into that tub and filled it right up.

It was the *smells* of hog killin that got to me the worst, but I swore and be derned if I's gonna let on, specially around Willie. So me and Delmer carried pans of blood and tubs of guts up to the women all day long. They had the kitchen turned into a sausage operation, a-grindin away, and tyin off them gut casings, til they had em *more* washtubs full of links of sausage ready for the smokehouse.

The work went on and on til we was all tuckered out, but we couldn't stop or the meat'd spoil. Ottus said you had to git it into the smokehouse right off. By dark we had the smokehouse partitioned off with a hickory fire a-curin hams and shoulders on one side, and the other side full of salted meat.

The women was renderin lard, and making cracklins, and sausage and blood sausage, an I don't know what all. The funny thing was, I had thought while I was workin that hog killin that I'd never eat again, especially not pork. But when we come up to the house that night and Lora offered me a little dish of cracklins, I took and et ever bite like a starvin man. So did Bernard and Delmer. An it tasted mighty good. I reckon it wasn't so different from eatin Granny's fried chicken after you'd saw her drape its neck acrost a tree root and then hold onto its head so she could chop it off. Maybe we wasn't so delicate after all, leastways not for town boys.

Chapter Ten

IT WAS A WET SPRING, which promised a second year in a row of delayed planting. Incessant rain clouds hung over Wills County like a metaphor for the unresolved chute burning cases. The governor, alarmed at the recent Night Riding activity in the western half of the state, launched a campaign against the vigilante group, offering a bounty of five hundred dollars for information leading to the arrest of those responsible for the attacks. Though the 1921 market closed with reasonable prices being paid for quality tobacco, Wills County's April court term hovered on the horizon. The farmers charged with arson felt threatened with all the ramifications of a prolonged jail sentence. On the other side, the tobacconists were taunted by the mocking echo of Judge Wingate's increasingly hollow vows to bring the Night Riders to justice.

Into such an atmosphere Lora's third baby was born. Lora hugged the bedpost as Ola took a rolling pin to her lower back.

Oh Ola, I wisht I's brave like you, she moaned. Lora was the baby of the Oakley family, and shrank from pain with the wistfulness of one who has always been tenderly comforted.

You're plenty brave, darlin. You done proved that twice before. Now, jist take it a step at a time. Ottus'll soon be back with Doctor Barton, and before you know it you'll be holdin this little un in your arms. Then I'll make you a cup of sassafras tea to build your blood back up, and anything you fancy to eat. Now won't that be nice, shug?

Four hours later when Ruth Drew left Ernest in charge of the children to run over under a dripping umbrella and check on Lora's progress, she was just in time. With Ola holding one of her feet, and Ruth the other, Lora gave a heave that felt like she was turning herself inside-out, and delivered into Dr. Barton's hands a dark-haired daughter. As soon as Lora and the baby were washed, Ola grabbed the umbrella and ran down to where Ottus had just slopped the pigs.

He put his tobacco pouch back into his pocket and hurried with Ola up to the house. Though he had been secretly hoping for a boy for practical reasons, when he looked at his new baby girl he forgot that hope completely.

Won't Adell be pleased? said Lora, stroking the baby's face and holding her close.

I'm pleased myself, Ottus answered, giving Lora a look as tender as the spring rain outside the open window. What're we gonna call her?

Don't you member what we decided if it was a girl? Madine. Transferring the baby's tightly gripped fist from her finger to Ottus's, she said, Madine Drew, this here's your daddy.

※　※　※　※　※　※　※　※　※　※　※

There had been so much rain lately that Ola had lost several chicks. They would drown under the hens' wings if she wasn't right there at the start of a storm to shoo them into the henhouse. Ninnies! she thought as she ran towards them on yet another rainy day in late March. A dead chick ain't no earthly good to nothin but predators, and I *ain't* keeping chickens to fatten up hawks and owls.

She kept a single barrel shotgun hanging beside the axe on the wall of the dogtrot during the daytime. The hens always let her know with a sharp squawk when a hawk or a fox was near, and Ola was quick to get to her gun. She generally missed, but the report alone was enough to scare it off.

Powerless over the weather, Ernest was sat at the kitchen table playing a jig for the children when Ola came in soaking wet and carrying a chicken. Ernest cut off his tune as she said, This un's got the limberneck.

So I see, he replied, and Fred stopped chasing flies with the fly swatter to stare at the way the chicken's head draped over his mother's arm.

Is it sick, Mama? asked Ethelyn.

Yes it is, hon. Go git me the broom.

What for? asked Fred. You gonna beat it on to death?

He asked the question in a tone so matter-of-fact that his parents looked at each other and laughed.

No Fred, I aim to fix it.

But how can you fix it with a broom?

You jist watch and you'll see, said Ernest, fetching the turpentine bottle from the cabinet and setting it on the table.

Here, Fred, said Ola as Ethelyn came up to her with the broom. Pull me out a long straw.

But I'm doin' the broom! Ethelyn protested.

You fetched it. Now it's Fred's turn to help, said Ola, and Fred up-ended the broom officiously, knocking his little sister to the floor in the process. She began to bawl and Ernest reached over and swatted Fred's bottom as hard as he could. Soon all three children were wailing, Ralph joining in for good measure.

I'm gonna whale the tar outa ever one of you if you don't hush up! cried Ola as the chicken flapped and struggled in her arms.

Here, said Ernest, picking Ralph up off the floor, and handing Ola the broomstraw Fred was clutching. Here now! All of you hush and watch your mama cure the sick chicken. He scooped Ethelyn up and settled her on his other knee, soothing and petting his two youngest.

Fred moved closer to Ola, too interested in the proceedings to pout over his spanking. He watched carefully as Ola reached over the chicken and uncorked the bottle of turpentine. Then she dipped the broomstraw into it and thrust it as far as she could down one of the chicken's nostrils.

Ooooooh, Ethelyn squealed in disgust, forgotten tears still on her cheeks.

Fred was chewing intently at his lower lip. How come that don't kill it? he asked.

What don't kill ya'll cure ya, like they always say, Ola replied.

It don't kill it cause your mama's a old hand at it, that's why. You better hope *you* don't never git the limberneck, said Ernest, lolling his head over to one side and making them laugh.

In just a few minutes the chicken amazed the children by drawing its head up straight and jumping down from Ola's lap. It strutted around the floor as if nothing had ever happened.

What'd I tell you? Ernest said, as Ethelyn and then Ralph squirmed down off his lap to join Fred in crawling after the chicken under and around the table. He went over and pulled Ola up into his arms. She's a authentic chicken doctor.

Ola laughed, and he held her against him, muttering into her hair, Ain't nothin your mama cain't fix if she takes a notion to. Nothin in this world.

❊ ❊ ❊ ❊ ❊ ❊ ❊ ❊ ❊ ❊ ❊

Early in April Willie's wife, Joetta, died of childbed fever. Dr. Barton telephoned Brother Walker, who offered to take Ola and Lora to Willie's house in his buggy. In the end, since Lora was only just up from the childbed herself, it was decided that Ola would go alone to help Joetta's mother dress the body.

Bring me back the baby to nurse, said Lora, if Willie wants me to, of course. Ola nodded, grim-faced, and climbed into the buggy beside Brother Walker.

But they arrived at the farmhouse only to find that the baby, too, had died, and Willie, in a deranged state, had left the house. Joetta's mother, Mrs. Elliott, was beside herself. Ola looked over at the form beneath the blanket, and at the small form under a receiving blanket in the bassinet, and decided to attend to the living first.

Do you have any idea where Willie might've gone to? Brother Walker was asking the distraught old woman. But she just shook her head and cried. I'll go lookin for him, Brother Walker said to Ola. I'll be back quick as I can.

Ola put her arms around Mrs. Elliott, saying, There, there, over and over. When Mrs. Elliott's sobs grew quieter Ola asked gently, Where are the children?

Tom an Wilma's got em. They don't know yet that she's…

Ola resumed her rocking and patting as Mrs. Elliott's sobs rebuilt themselves. The house was dark and smelled of death. The animals needed to be seen to. Ola was besieged by how much there was to attend to all at the same time. Noticing that several chairs had been brought into the room, she steered the stricken woman toward them.

After a moment Mrs. Elliott began talking to her again. He's… I don't mean no disre-disrespect, Ola… She gave a tearing gasp. Willie ain't right… he's… he ain't right.

Ola froze, her heart starting to pound. Lemme light us a lamp, Miz Elliott, and then we'll set and talk a minute. Can I git you some coffee, or water or something? She busied herself, opening a window, and putting a pot of coffee on the stove. When she returned to the bedroom, Mrs. Elliott stared up at her with eyes that were the incarnation of pain. Ola sat beside her and took her hand. What is it, Miz Elliott? What has Willie done?

When… when Joetta was dyin … wasn't nobody but me and him in this room with her. Dr. Barton had got called away to a accident. And Willie, he… he wouldn't… let her… close her eyes. She subsided into sobs again.

What? Ola asked. What do you mean?

When she was composed enough to speak, she said, He got up and stood over her, and he… he *took aholt of her eyelids and helt em open*. I said… I said, 'Leave her be! What're you doin?' But he jist put his face right over hers, and says, 'She'll want my face to be the last thing she sees.' And… and I was scared of him, Ola. I's too scared to fight him. I don't think he's right in the head. Nobody's right in the head that'd do such a thing as that. So my little girl had to *die* with him a-holdin her *eyes* open!

Mrs. Elliott fell to crying again with such despair Ola couldn't speak. She looked again at the form under the blanket, knowing they must prepare it for burial. She would do what was necessary, but she needed some time after this revelation. For right now she couldn't move.

Finally, staring down at the half empty coffee cup in her lap, unable to recall having drunk any of it, Ola turned to Mrs. Elliott. Would you rather I manage in here while you do up them dishes in yonder?

The older woman grabbed Ola's hand in mild alarm and shook her head. Oh no. No, I couldn't do that, Ola. I couldn't leave her now. Ola nodded, making a seam of her lips to keep them from trembling. Then she carried the coffee cups into the kitchen, and went out to the cistern to draw water for the washing of the bodies.

* * * * * * * * * * *

Brother Walker found Willie shooting his rifle into the trees beyond the back pasture of the farm he rented. By the time he brought him back, the little house was filling up with neighbors and family members. Joetta lay in the bed with her baby beside her.

Mrs. Elliott had closed her daughters' eyes with the tenderest touch Ola had ever seen. Then she and Mrs. Elliott had washed and changed Joetta, and put clean sheets on the bed. Ola kept busy, even after people started coming in.

However, soon after Rudy and Faye arrived Ola grew still, watching closely as Brother Walker led Willie into the kitchen. The preacher held him by the elbow. Willie looked dishevelled and dazed, his kinky blonde hair all on end from an unconscious gesture of running his hand through it repeatedly. Without speaking, he stared at all the people in the room.

Willie, I'm so sorry, she said quietly, touching his arm. He looked at her as if he didn't know her. We need to order a coffin.

Order *hell*! he snapped. Then he turned and left again by the back door.

Brother Walker shook his head. Don't worry, Ola, I'll stay with him.

No, Brother Walker, she said. I'll git Rudy to go with him. You're needed here. She indicated Mrs. Elliott, who was sitting near the bed, staring in raw grief at her daughter's face.

At her request, Rudy followed Willie down to the barn, where they built a coffin from some old planks that were propped against the side of the building. The funeral was held there in the house the next day, and Mrs. Elliott took Willie and Joetta's two children to live with her for awhile, to give Willie time to git his bearings as she put it.

Ola never told anyone what Mrs. Elliott had said about Willie's behavior at Joetta's deathbed. It was too bizarre, too frightening. She stored it up, unspoken, alongside her worry for Hazel. Unless she had to for some unfathomable reason, Ola vowed to herself, she would *never* tell it, not even to Ernest or Lora.

* * * * * * * * * * *

Ernest always said the same thing when each court term rolled around. Ain't no need to go worrying about it. It'll fall out jist like it done the last time. No witnesses, no case.

Ola knew he believed what he said, but she also knew he was relieved when each term ended and the newspapers printed the usual statement that the cases against the men accused of burning the tobacco chute had been continued.

When it happened again in mid-April, Ola said, I jist don't see why they don't drop it altogether. Why do they keep on continuing em?

Judge Wingate's gotta let it die out gradual-like. He's been blowing off steam for over a year now about how he intends to prosecute the Night Riders. Even the governor's watching him, after sending in them troops and all at Wingate's insistence. Hell, Wingate was looking to win points with this all over the state, so he cain't jist drop it.

Well I'm sick and tired of it, she said, hanging wet diapers on the line Ernest had strung for her on the back porch. It was raining again, and he sat in an old straw-bottom ladder-back whittling stakes out of a cedar branch. What does Ray say about it?

Ernest shifted uneasily. Upon joining the Night Riders he'd had to take a solemn oath never to divulge any of what went on at their meetings. Ernest had never let this stop him from talking to Ola about some aspects of it, but lately Ray had re-emphasized the oath of secrecy, making it clear it applied to wives, brothers, parents—everyone. He had actually pulled Ernest aside after the last meeting, warning him specifically not to discuss Night Rider activities with Ola.

Ernest, I know how close y'all are to Ottus Drew, Ray had said when no one else was within earshot. Now I don't need to remind you that he's non-Association. Ola could accidentally let stuff slip to her sister. Jist lemme remind you of the importance of keeping quiet, even around your wife.

Chafing at the memory, Ernest said to Ola, He says the same thing I say. She looked at him, waiting. There ain't no more to say.

Maybe not, she replied after a moment, stabbing another clothespeg onto another diaper.

I got to go out tonight, he said, not looking at her.

She didn't respond for a few minutes as she finished hanging the diapers. Then, as if he hadn't spoken, she said, The children'll be wakin up soon. Keep a eye on em. She slipped some clothespegs into her apron pocket, and went down the back porch steps, running through the rain across the yard, and disappearing into the henhouse. Ernest watched as she emerged, carrying a chicken. Bringing the old hen a little distance from the henhouse, she took hold of its nobbly head and gave a sudden twist, feeling the snap of the bones as much as hearing it. She twisted again and again as if wringing water from a rag, then pulled hard.

When the head came off, the chicken's body slid to the ground and lurched about the yard, spurting blood. Ola threw the head over the fence into the pasture. When the body stopped flopping and slumped over, she pinned it upside down by its feet onto the clothesline, then stooped to wipe the worst of the blood from her hands onto the wet grass.

❄ ❄ ❄ ❄ ❄ ❄ ❄ ❄ ❄ ❄ ❄

Ola was awakened one night in late May by a series of muffled thumps out in the dogtrot. Her eyes flew open. It took her a moment to come awake and remember that Ernest was out. Someone was groping his way through the dark towards her. A fumbling at the door and he entered the room. She lay still, her heart hammering. She thought of her shotgun up over the mantel, but there was absolutely no light in the room.

Eventually the man cleared his throat and Ola knew it was Ernest. Soft sounds told her he was clumsily stripping off his clothes and dropping them on the floor. Then he climbed in beside her and fell almost immediately to sleep, each snore lifting a faint incense of moonshine and tobacco.

The next day Ernest went about his work silently, his jaw set. He had no patience with the children, no teasing for Ola. In the early afternoon, as soon as she had cleared up the dishes, she put Ralph in the buggy and set off for Lora's. Fred pulled Ethelyn in his wagon for awhile, then ordered her out, saying she was too heavy. Ola let her sit on the end of the buggy, facing her. She dangled her legs down and sang Row Row Row Your Boat over and over.

The road was soft with recent rain, the pushing hard. By the time they got there, Ralph was asleep and Ethelyn drowsy.

Lora was out on the porch with Mrs. January, James's widowed mother who lived on the next farm to Lora and Ottus's. Lora's three were napping and Ethelyn seemed happy enough to join them. Fred went off to play by himself among the outbuildings.

Watch out for that old well! Ola called after him.

Ottus done boarded that over, said Lora. I don't think he could fall down in it if he wanted to.

Well he might jist want to; you never know with boys, said Ola and they all laughed.

Mrs. January had been into Greenberry that morning and had a copy of the *DAILY LEAF* on her lap. Ola, she said, handing it to her, you might wanna read this piece here.

Ola read the headline she pointed to: *Masked Night Riders Visit McDermott Family, Whip, Order to Leave.* She looked up at Lora, who said nothing, but who regarded her with a steady, serious expression. The other women sat quiet as Ola read the article.

A band of armed men numbering between thirty and fifty visited a home on the Tennessee border of Wills County last night around midnight. They whipped the widow who owns the farm, a Mrs. Annie McDermott, as well as her daughter and son-in-law. Mrs. McDermott's old, blind father was allowed to hold his great grandson off to one side while the beatings were administered.

The family was ordered to 'leave the country' and it appears that they did so within a few hours. It is said that the family has a bad reputation for thievery and a generally questionable moral character. Sheriff Jones and his deputies are investigating. They have recovered some stolen property from the place.

James was feeling poorly last night, Mrs. January said, as if apropos of nothing. I give him a dose a mineral water and he's better this morning.

Ola handed the paper back to her and said nothing.

Ottus says he's gonna have his little brother Delmer come out and help us set the tobacco this year, Lora said, in an effort to change the subject. All this rain's gonna give us such a late start, we'll need us the extry help.

Ola nodded, and replied absent-mindedly, That'll be good.

After a few more minutes of stiff conversation, Mrs. January struggled to her feet, saying, Well, I best be gittin on back. Left my wash boiling away yonder. Jist thought y'all might wanna see this.

Much obliged, Miz January, said Lora, as the older woman started off down the road. As soon as she was out of earshot, the starch went out of the air between the two sisters.

Ernest come in late last night, Ola admitted quietly. They been having a lot of meetings here lately.

He say anything?

Ola shook her head. He ain't supposed to, you know. But he's been in some mood all day long. *That* sorta crap ain't what he signed on for.

I know, said Lora. Ernest never woulda taken no beatin part in something like that.

Don't let's talk about it. Ola took out her snuffbox. But you know, if I did feel like talking about it, I'd ask Ernest if James January was there. I know she's trying to make out like he wasn't. Lora gave a knowing smirk. People beat all, don't they? I'll go git you a coffee can. Want a cup of coffee?

No thanks, shug. I preciate the offer though.

When Lora went inside, Ola stopped fidgeting with her snuffbox, and stared frowning out over the empty tobacco fields.

* * * * * * * * * * *

Some fifteen miles away a Model T Ford drove south along the Paris Road towards the McDermott place. Arch and Ted Wingate, and two of the more prominent tobacconists were driving down to take a look.

Ted Wingate knew exactly where it was since he held the mortgage on the farm. He had been planning to foreclose anyway, and was in an uncharacteristically light mood. The Night Riders had done him a service without realizing it by running off the shiftless McDermotts. Now he had a new, undamaged property to list. Look at that, they didn't even burn down the barn, he noted to himself with satisfaction as they turned into the laneway.

The slamming of the four car doors echoed like shots through the empty frame house as the men got out. Ted Wingate went straight up the porch steps and inside, while the others wandered over to the trees in front of the house. Sure enough, hairy hemp ropes hung limp around the trunks of three of them.

Good God a'mighty, Cutter exclaimed, removing his pipe from his mouth as if it suddenly tasted bad.

They sure don't seem to care about leaving evidence behind, do they? Burns commented.

Unfortunately, Axton, these ropes only tell us what we already know, said the judge with an air of self-importance. Ever farmer in the county'd have this sorta rope in his possession. The only way to nail em is through eyewitness testimony. We gotta git the McDermotts to come back and testify against em, or else find a weak link among the Night Riders themselves. Divide and conquer.

Ted Wingate heard his brothers's remarks through the broken window of the front room. Noting the unbroken panes were none too clean, he crunched his way across the floor. These farmhouses are all the same, he muttered contemptuously, two rooms and a path.

The McDermotts had packed up in a hurry. They'd left some broken sticks of furniture here and there, some clothes heaped in a corner, and several half-empty jars and bottles in the cabinet. The banker opened the pantry door beside the cookstove and found a white enamel slop jar with a dead mouse in it. He shook his head and walked out onto the back porch. There a table stood under a small, fly-specked mirror. A razor strap hung on a nail.

Wingate heard Arch and the others enter the house by the front door as he crossed the backyard to the smokehouse. Any meat the McDermotts had put by had been taken from the nails along the center beam. But they'd left a string of onions and a bunch of weeds hanging upside-down on one of the walls. He walked across the pocked dirt floor, wary of snakes, and sniffed at the dried weeds. They were surprisingly aromatic, treating him to an instant memory of his mother's savory chicken stew.

From the smokehouse he walked over to the stable, where he stopped suddenly at the open door. Another half second and he'd have walked right through a large spiderweb. Picking up a haystraw, he raked it down with a deft, economic gesture, not noticing the spider that dropped to the ground and scurried away. He lit a match and peered into the gloom. It was empty except for a cat and her mewling, squirming mound of kittens. Vaguely repulsed, the banker blew out the match and made his way across a muddy field to the dark fire barn.

This door, too, was open, and hung slightly crooked, one corner of it mired in the mud. He looked up through the empty tiers, satisfied at how little light bled through from outside. It looked like a sound barn.

By the time their search was completed and Arch backed his car onto the road and turned north toward Greenberry, Ted's thoroughly good mood was in sharp contrast with that of the others.

If we don't deal with these hooligans in the June term *this* year, we'll have no credibility left with the governor nor anybody else, Arch grumbled.

Call in a outside judge and jury, his brother replied in a detached tone.

Cutter leaned forward. I do believe that's what's needed, Ted. Good idea. No reflection on *your* strategies of course, Arch.

The judge sighed, as if coming to a reluctant conclusion. A small flame of anger towards his brother smouldered beneath his response. Well, I've thought of that. But I'll tell you one thing. If we gotta have outsiders in it'd better be somebody I can count on. Judge Brebner over in Woodward County oughta do. He owes me.

Burns reached up to pat Arch on the shoulder. It's liable to be a rough ride, but the good citizens of Greenberry's right behind you.

Don't waste your time worrying about me—I'll git the bastards, said Arch.

Ted smiled to himself and said nothing.

Chapter Eleven

SOON AS SCHOOL LET OUT on the Third Monday of May, me and some of the other boys took ourselves down to the court square like usual to git in on the excitement. There was a lection comin up and we knowed what that meant: free tablets of paper, free pocket mirrors, free pencils. Wasn't no tellin what you might git during a lection campaign. So we was on the lookout for hand-outs as we walked around amongst the wagons and crowds.

The big water trough on the corner of 7th Street and South was about all that was left of the old days. The animals could still get em a drink there at least. Right behind that, ol Uncle Jerry, the biggest bootlegger in town, was havin him a game of checkers with Horace McDade, who was one of the Night Riders that was indicted for the chute burnin. Right near them, Rudy Oakley was doin his barberin as usual. We was jist walking by when we seen Sammy Smythe comin towards em. Sammy Smythe was a slicked up, pig-faced man in a white suit who was always runnin for public office. This year he was lookin to become mayor. Sure enough, he was carryin him a sack full of giveaways. So we sidled up behind him and waited our chance.

Hello there, boys! he sang out real hearty-like to Rudy and them. I'm sure I can count on y'all to put me in office on lection day.

Rudy never even looked up from Ronnie Doyle's straw-bale of a head, when he said, Where'd you ever git a idee like that from, Sammy?

The rest of em fell about like Rudy was a great joker, but Mr. Smythe, he was ready for em. Cause I can help you boys out in the courtroom is why.

That got their attention alright. Rudy stopped his scissors in mid-air and said, Now, what good would a mayor be in a courtroom, Sammy? Influence, said Mr. Smythe. Then he lowered his voice and made a big show of lookin left and right, which drew several other Night Riders over, like James January and Asa Miller who'd been negotiating a trade nearby. Mr. Miller was another one who was indicted.

Ed Franklin's runnin for circuit judge, and me and him's like brothers, Sammy Smythe was sayin in a excited whisper. He's a shoo-in for the position, and if I can give him the right incentive, why he says he'll oil these unfortunate cases through the system in jig time. Then we can put all this mess behind us, which is right where it belongs if you ask me.

What exactly do you mean by 'the right incentive'? asked Mr. McDade, gittin up from his checker game and joining in the conversation.

A mere thirty-eight dollars for each man that's been indicted is what I figger it at.

Rudy spat a stream of tobacco juice onto the sidewalk and cut his metallic, blue eyes back to Mr. Smythe.

I ain't askin nothin for my part, only ninety dollars for expenses. Franklin wants two thousand, and believe me, boys, that's cheap as these things go.

Thirty-eight dollars is a right smart if you ask me, said James January, receivin a general chorus of assent. What're these so-called expenses you say you got?

Well, I cain't put the money into the bank around here. I'd have to go up to St. Louis or someplace to put through your checks—unless of course you all pay in cash.

What if Franklin don't git elected? Rudy asked.

Mr. Smythe laughed, as if that was a impossibility. He's already Commonwealth Attorney. Oh he's in it—he'll be part of this one way or another, don't you think he won't. We could both serve your all's interests better from these positions we're runnin for, but he'll be *servin* you, believe me, in any case. You all'd be doin yourselves a big favor by takin up this offer.

The farmers looked at each other. Finally Asa Miller said, I think we need more of a sure thing before puttin up money.

You don't think Ed Franklin's got the connections to do a little thing like *this*, then you don't know how the system works. All that's required is thirty-eight dollars a head. Less'n that if your comrades who weren't indicted chip in and support you. Mr. Smythe looked at Cluster Higgins, who frowned and started shufflin around like he's uncomfortable.

It's damn chicken-feed, boys, for what it'll do. Think about it. But don't take too long decidin, in case Franklin changes his mind. Oh, and by the way, he said, handin around little note tablets that had his picture on em and said Vote Smythe for Mayor, Uh...Franklin don't wanna be approached on this. That way it ain't so obvious. He's authorized me to handle everything, so, if you're writin out checks, jist make em out to yours truly. That's Smythe with a Y: S-M-Y-T-H-E. You have it on your tablets there. I'll be in touch. And remember, mum's the word.

Rudy hadn't taken a tablet, so Mr. Smythe leaned over and tucked one in his overalls pocket before goin on his way. I could tell Rudy didn't appreciate it by the way he froze for a second and clenched his jawbone. But we got us one, and went lookin for pencils to go with it from other candidates. The next time we passed by that corner all a them Night Riders was gone.

* * * * * * * * * *

Me and Delmer didn't bust out of school quite so happy as usual when summer vacation started in 1921. We stood up against the school buildin waitin out a thunderstorm and yellin over the rain. He was upset cause he was havin to go work on his brother Ottus's farm for a few weeks early in the summer. As for me, I'd jist been told I'd failed the fourth grade. Now I's gonna have to be in Fairy's class with her and Hunter's sister, Mary Emily, and all of them little babies. It worried Hollis, too, cause who was he gonna sit with and all?

At least we'll all still git to play together at recess. That's what counts, Hunter yelled over the rain.

That's right, Delmer added. Class work's awful no matter who you got beside of you. But it ain't as bad as gall-derned *farm* work.

I didn't say much, jist stood there a-watchin them rain drops throw up little crown-like splashes in the standin water. I felt like Noah on the watch for dry land and losin hope of ever gittin offa that ark they called school.

When it let up enough for us to start for home, Delmer kicked a stone so hard it bounced off a car fender parked in front of the house we was passing. A man come to the door and started out after us, yellin like the dickens. So we took a short-cut, splashin up mud all over us. The excitement shook us outa ourselves for a little while, and we got to laughin some then. We went on over to Boxtown and got ourselves up a muddy game a shinny with George Adams and some of his brothers and I forgot all about school.

☆　☆　☆　☆　☆　☆　☆　☆　☆　☆　☆

The day Ottus and Lora come in the wagon for Delmer, me and Hollis was playin marbles in my front yard, taking advantage of a break in the weather. I's jist about to shoot for Purgatory with my cat-eye when we seen em go by. They waved, and I said, Let's go! Delmer's leavin' out.

We charged around the corner jist in time to see Aunt Ruth leadin him out to the wagon, with her arm around his shoulders. Granny was asking Ottus and Lora to visit with em awhile, but they said they had to git back. Delmer shuffled along real sulky-like. He was stuffin that red top of his into a tote sack. We heard Aunt Ruth say, Listen, hon, two weeks'll go by real fast. Here's what I want you to do. I want you to pick me some of them June apples. They'll be jist right for pickin in two weeks, and I'll make you the best apple pie that ever *was* the very day you git back here. Okay?

He jist shrugged, and she kept on a-talkin at him. Did you ever know I planted that old June apple tree when I was carrying Ottus? It'uz away back yonder and it's been the best little tree. She hugged him and it was easy to see she was about ready to cry. Delmer was holdin hisself real stiff. He throwed his tote sack onto the wagon next to some boxes of groceries I reckoned they'd got from Uncle Berry's, then clumb on up after it and set facin backwards with his bare feet a-danglin down.

Fairy and Debry was making on over the baby in Lora's arms, and Ottus said, Y'all stand back now. Bye, Ma! Bye, Granny! He clicked to the mule and give it a lick with the reins and off they went, ever'body hollerin good-bye. Lora yelled to Delmer to keep aholt of Harry, who was wantin to set beside of his boy uncle on the back of the wagon.

We was yelling bye to Delmer, but I don't think he could hear us in all the commotion. He waved though, first to Aunt Ruth and them, then at us, while we raced the wagon on around the corner and up 14th Street.

After they'd gone, me and Hollis ran back and flopped onto my front steps all out of breath. Once I could talk again I said to him, What do you wanna do now?

Let's play war. I'll be the South and you be the North. I always had to be the North, cause Hollis said his granpa'd skin him alive if he ever heard tell of him playin like he was a yankee.

So we shot our way across town from opposite sides of the street, snipin from behind bushes and birdbaths. We scared a cat up a tree and set all the dogs to barkin and follerin along. When we moved into the short-cut world of backyards, old ladies yelled at us as they lifted laundry up to their clotheslines, and chickens went demented over my cap gun.

But the best was Mr. Peavey. He was a whiskery old geezer that folks said was *in* the Civil War hisself. He was on the Confederate side, but he'd had a brother that'd fought for the Union. They'd both been at Shiloh, and his brother had got killed there. Some folks said Mr. Peavey had shot him hisself, but Mama said that was nonsense—jist eedjits letting their imaginations run wild to beef up a story that was sad enough the way it stood.

But that day old Mr. Peavey was jist comin out of his outhouse when we caught him in our crossfire, and you'd a swore he'd been shot for real the way he took on, a-clutchin at his heart and fallin back against the privy door. He had this little whistle in his gaspin that I hadn't never heard in nobody's breathin before. But the minute he could, he give us what-for. He run us outa his yard like we was the enemy sure nough. Hollis said later maybe that was the rebel yell he give out, and I said if it sounded like that now, and him with one foot in the grave, jist imagine what it musta sounded like when he was in the war and surrounded by other fellers all makin that same cry.

I reckon we was so rattled ourselves after that that we didn't watch which way we's goin, cause we ended up in the middle of the next block at a place we'd never even knowed was there before. It was a low red brick wall, with no gate in it at all, boxin up a little family cemetery. What in tarnation's this? Look, it's a old graveyard, Hollis said, stating the obvious and answerin his own question into the bargain.

We clumb over into it and I started readin them tomb rocks out loud: John Smith, 1792. Boy, that's a old un. Looked like they's all Smiths: Sarah, Ann, Wesley, Abbey, Stewart.... Then I come to one in a corner that was different. It was poured out of cement stead of carved out of stone, and it didn't have no name nor date like all a them others. Somebody had scratched out by hand on it: John Smith's concubine.

I asked Hollis what was a concubine, but he jist shrugged and said, Beats me. Let's play like I've captured you and this is my prison camp. But it started to rain again shortly after that, so we jist went on home, seein if we could run between the raindrops.

That night at supper I asked Mama what a concubine was. Well I sure wasn't prepared for how this'd take her. She got red as a beet and landed me a smack across the face that dern near knocked me out of my chair. It left my ear jist a-ringin. She never did say a word, jist went back to eatin her white beans and cornbread. Bridget Ruth kept her eyes down, but Papa and Bernard, they laughed. Then Papa said, Nell, I like the way you explained that to that boy. He got so tickled he liked to never got control. Bout the time he'd sober up he'd say, That's what I like about the South, or something like that, and set hisself off all over again.

As for me, I figured I'd have to look it up in the school dictionary next fall. Whatever it was, it wasn't safe to bring up around home. But it was mighty important, that was for sure.

* * * * * * * * * *

The rain seemed to let up after Delmer left, and ever'body was sayin thank goodness cause it meant the plantin could go ahead. So I reckoned he was workin hard at it out yonder in the country.

I was even asked to do some work myself when Uncle Berry took inventory over at the grocery. He locked the door and put the Closed sign in the window, and him and Bernard and Raymond Luther, his butcher, they all had em a stock sheet and a pencil to count up exactly what was on the shelves. Mr. Luther was back in the meat section, of course, and Uncle Berry was doin the candy counter, since he said he reckoned it'd be cruel to ask us kids to help with that. It felt funny bein in the store with no customers, and I wasn't usually allowed back behind the counter. It was a Friday. Delmer had been gone a week and the June court session was due to start up that next Monday. You'll understand why I can remember them things when I tell you what happened.

Bernard was up a ladder countin the cans and such, and I was settin down below him on a barrel with our stock sheet. My job was to write the number beside of the item on the sheet when he called it out. It wasn't my idea of fun, but Uncle Berry had said he'd give me a quarter for it, and that sorta opportunity didn't come along all that often. Besides, Mama and Papa would've skinned me alive if I hadn't a done it. Back in them days a kid didn't really have a choice, even when it looked like he did. Leastways I didn't.

The stock sheet was alphabetical, but them cans wasn't arranged that away on the shelves. So when Bernard called out a thing I had to run my pencil down the list and find it. Which wasn't always easy. You take pork n beans for instance. Why they's three sizes of that: number three, number two and number one. That messed me up for awhile, but then we got to doin alright. Number three pie peaches and number three table peaches was beside one another on the shelf *and* on the list, so I got to feelin good along through there.

Number two okra and tomatoes, Bernard said, eight cans. I wrote me a eight beside of that, and was ready to hear Number three yellow sweet potatoes next. But instead he said, Number two white wax cherries, four cans. Then he said, Number two black raspberries, three cans, but I still hadn't found them cherries, so I was gittin all bumfuzzled, and said, Wait a minute, and then Bernard started to git frustrated, and I could hear Uncle Berry behind us, mutterin to hisself, trying to keep count of all a them candies.

Well, things was gittin kindly intense when there come a poundin at the door. The shade was pulled down and Uncle Berry roared out, Closed for takin inventory!

But the knocking kept up and then we heard Mr. Hayden, from the Boarding House across the street yellin, *Open up, Berry! Open up!*

So Uncle Berry he got up, all impatient-like and opened the door. Mr. Hayden was a old, white-haired man, and he was all outa breath. They's a big fight on up at the Courthouse, he puffed out. Ed Franklin's done lit into Sammy Smythe and they say they're rollin around in the dirt like schoolboys! I already sent Gunther around to hitch up your wagon—let's git on up there!

There wasn't no arguin with that. We dropped our sheets and pencils and done like he said. It was only a few blocks away and we found us a space where we could pull in right in front of the Confederate monument. There was a fight going on sure nough. We'd got there jist as Deputy Meshew busted through the crowd that was around em. We had us a good view up on that wagon, and Mr. Hayden was right. Ed Franklin, who was a little bitty, stripey suit sort of a man, he was a-straddlin Mr. Smythe and poundin the daylights out of him. Ever'body was laughin and shoutin. Tom Duffy from the livery stable run and clumb up onto the back of our wagon next to Gunther so he could see better, and told how Mr. Smythe'd been a-settin there having a smoke on the bench part of the Confederate monument, when Mr. Franklin come along and clobbered him backwards right off of it and started whalin the tar out of him.

Uncle Berry shushed Tom Duffy when Deputy Meshew got the two of em upright. Ever'body got quiet then so they could hear. It wasn't no trouble hearin Ed Franklin. He was so mad he was screamin. *Arrest him!* he ordered the Deputy. He looked like he's about ready for Hopkinsville—meaning the asylum. Them eyes was a-poppin out of his head and his skinny neck was jist ropey with veins.

Then Mr. Smythe, all offended-like, a-pullin and dustin at his jacket, said, You're the one that oughta be arrested! He was looking pretty beat-up in his dirty white suit. His lip was split and bleedin and his whole face was red and sorta swole up.

Listen, Smythe, Mr. Franklin yelled, you're guilty of slanderin my name *and* of runnin a bribery scheme with the Night Riders! That's a federal offense and I intend to see that you go to prison! He was stabbin at Mr. Smythe with his finger like it was a knife. You will not destroy my good reputation as a man of honor!

Deputy Meshew had aholt of both their arms and he kept tryin to calm em down. But Mr. Smythe, he pulled back and said, Believe me, Ed, no one wants to git to the bottom of this more than me. *You* are the one who's goin to jail—for assault and battery. Now, I am goin home to clean myself up, and then we will sort this out. I'll meet you in Sheriff Jones' office in... (Here he pulled up his pocket watch, which was swingin loose in front of his vest on its chain) ...in precisely one hour.

He turned and walked away in the direction of the Appleby place on South 7th, where he rented a room. When the deputy went inside the Courthouse with Mr. Franklin, people started breakin into little groups and tellin the story to one another as if the folks beside em hadn't been right there and saw the whole thing for theirselves. I heard Moses Galbraith, the Courthouse janitor, tellin Uncle Dave about it. Yessuh, it was a real knockdown-dragout.... Course Uncle Dave didn't git the pleasure of seein it, though he'd've heard ever word and prob'ly ever blow a-landin, too. Wasn't much got past Uncle Dave, blind and a hundred or no blind and a hundred.

We went on back to the store, thinkin the excitement was all over. Uncle Berry give us a dinner break, and we et us some crackers and cheese and pickles, settin around on barrels and recountin the fight. This part of inventoryin was fun, specially when he give us root beers to drink and our pick of the candy counter for dessert. Jist don't take nothin from them Rutter Scotch Hearts on over to the other side, cause I done counted all of them.

We finished up eatin and got on back to work. But about the time me and Bernard was all done the kraut and was movin towards the pepper sauce, here come Mr. Hayden a-hammerin at the door again. It was about two o'clock and he'd hung around the Sheriff's office to see the next chapter of the story unfold. And what a chapter it turned out to be, cause Sammy Smythe never showed up!

We didn't git to go back to the Courthouse though. This time Mr. Hayden jist set and told us what'd happened. It took em awhile, he said, but they finally got old Appleby in to testify that Smythe had caught the 12:47 to Memphis. Sheriff Jones give Deputy Meshew proper hell about lettin him git away, but ever'body agreed he couldn't've knowed. Hell *nobody* had figured on that rascally Smythe actually skippin town!

It had Greenberry in a uproar. The next day's *DAILY LEAF* sold out of its entire edition by noon and they had to run a reprint. All anybody could say was how they's *bound* to catch him, especially now ever'body in the county had a stack of pictures of him on their note tablets. But when they called Memphis to have the police meet the train, they said he wasn't on it, musta got off somewheres in between. He was provin to be slipperier'n they thought Sammy Smythe could ever be. The amazin thing is that the chase went on for almost *two years* before a Greenberry man on vacation in Florida spotted old Sammy. He was settin on a park bench right out in the open, and lookin none too prosperous. So his fella citizen told a passin policeman, said, Yonder's a wanted man if you're interested, and they caught him at last. It was Deputy Meshew who was sent down to fetch him, and the two of em come back on the train, handcuffed together. Can you imagine what sorta trip that'd make? But I'm gittin ahead of my story.

First thing I done when I got home from my inventoryin job was drop my quarter down to the bottom corner of my pillow case. Then I tore off the top page of my election tablet and stuck it to the wall with some flour and water paste. I wrote WANTED: DEAD OR ALIVE acrost it and played like my bed was the sheriff's office, from the minute we's done supper til it was time to use it for sleepin.

The next day the paper sold out, and Papa said that he bet the only ones wasn't laughing was Ray Tibbs and the Night Riders. Old Judge Arch is bustin a gusset or two over this, you can be sure about that.

Ivy lives over by the Appleby's, Mama said, and Miz Appleby done told her Sammy Smythe had her husband carry him to catch the train down at Slayden's Crossing to avoid the Greenberry Depot. Said he rode the whole way down there on the floorboards underneath of a blanket!

After we all settled down again from a bout of hilarity, Papa said, Well he's the comic relief in the whole story. But all jokin aside, this June court term oughta be pretty hot. Cause now it ain't jist Wingate who's after the Night Riders. Now they got Ed Franklin vowin to git em too, so he can clear his name. And *he's* the damn Commonwealth Attorney.

Hardin. That was all Mama needed to say.

Scuze me, Nell. Then he got right back to his story. It says here, they plan to deal with this bribery and *assault* bidness now on Monday. But they got them chute burnin cases scheduled for June 27th—a week from Monday—and y'all mark my words, or most of em. (Here he winked at us kids.) They ain't gonna continue em *this* time.

Chapter Twelve

OTTUS PULLED THE LAST STOB OUT OF THE GROUND, and together the Drews and Lawrences, with Delmer to help, lifted the big canvas off the plant bed and carried it to one side, turning it over so it could dry out. Ernest said, Well, there's this year's crop for you, Ottus. Lotta tobacco to work, sure nough.

I reckon we cain't afford to wait long to reset em, said Ottus. Let's go on over and undress yours right away.

It's sorta like changing sheets on a bed, ain't it? said Lora, smiling up at Ottus as she took his hand for the walk across the L-shaped pattern of fields to Ernest and Ola's. He smiled at her.

Ola had Ralph and Madine in the baby carriage, and the other four children ran ahead, racing each other and stopping to float leaves in the puddles at the edge of the pasture. Delmer walked along feeling lonely and homesick until Ernest noticed and fell in beside him.

Think you'll make a farmer when you grow up, Del?

Delmer was surprised and secretly grateful for the attention, though he didn't much care for people calling him Del. Naw, he answered. I aim to go to work at the Woolen Mills soon's Ma lets me quit school.

What makes you wanna do that?

They got em a baseball team—a good un.

How can you be so sure you'll make the team? Ernest only meant to tease the boy, but Delmer gave him such a scowl that he realized this was a subject he'd better not handle lightly.

Suddenly Ernest dodged over to the orchard they were walking past and came back with a half-grown spartan. Here, catch! he called, arcing the apple in Delmer's direction. Delmer caught it, then threw it back to Ernest. They kept it up all the way, neither one missing a catch. When they lifted the canvas from the Lawrence plant bed, it seemed a bit lighter to Delmer than the first one had.

❊ ❊ ❊ ❊ ❊ ❊ ❊ ❊ ❊ ❊ ❊ ❊

They let the new shoots sit over Sunday. We'll begin the planting in the morning early, said Ottus, as he lifted Adell into the wagon bed beside Harry. Lora held the baby and sat up on the bench with Ottus. She wore a blue and white plaid dress with a wide blue sash. She had made Adell one just like it, tying her sash into a bow and pinning it on top of the little girl's bobbed hair. Ottus wore a dark suit and tie which he'd acquired at the time of his father's funeral and his own wedding. Harry had on black pants with suspenders that crossed at the back of his white Sunday shirt. Delmer climbed heavily onto the wagon wearing his Sunday shirt and the only pants he owned that weren't overalls—a pair of brown wool trousers too hot by half for June and scratchy as a brier.

They bounced over the roads to where the Hickory Methodist Church raised its white steeple beside the road to Paducah. The field next to the church was still set off with hitch-racks, though now there were several automobiles parked along one end. When people slammed their car doors, the mules and horses would pull sideways and protest.

People called out greetings to one another as they walked into church. Ernest and Ola were there, and Rudy and Faye with their three daughters. But Willie hadn't come to church since Joetta's death. Delmer overheard Lora tell someone that he was still living by himself while Mrs. Elliott cared for Silas and Joanie over at her son Tom's place.

The prayers that morning were all about the planting. Brother Walker read about rain on dry land, and the congregation rolled their eyes at each other. But the preacher said, The Lord knows how much rain he's sent. He knows it ain't dry land that's our problem this year. He sends ever'thing for our good, and He's done sent us a challenge here. He's watchin to see what we make out of it. The Lord is always testing us, and ever'thing we do is our answer to Him.

The farm families sat in the sweltering little church, fanning themselves as they listened. Proper cardboard fans as well as scraps of paper, even hymnbooks were pressed into the service of moving the heavy air that threatened to smother them all.

When everybody stood up to sing Count Your Blessings, Delmer, who had been watching a wasp bump into a window again and again, didn't join in. Still he was thrilled, despite himself, by the fancywork of the harmonies that soared above the tiny organ. Lora sang in a high voice on one side of him, and he could hear Ottus's rich tenor on the other.

They finished the service with The Unclouded Day. Delmer poured outside midstream in the river of worshippers, anxious to get back to Ottus's so he could change out of his scratchy pants. The congregation thinned to a trickle in front of Brother Walker. Delmer tried to slip past unnoticed, but felt a large hand on his head for just an instant. The boy gave the preacher a half nod and made for the wagon.

Lora and Ottus hung back, visiting at the church door. Harry followed Delmer and they petted the horses while they waited for the others. Suddenly the younger boy had an idea. Delmer, will you gimme a piggy-back ride?

Shoot, Harry, you're dern near as big as me. I couldn't pick you up on my back.

Harry giggled at his child-uncle. Yes you could. Please, Delmer?

So he squatted down and let Harry climb onto his back. Holding the little boy's legs around his waist, Delmer galloped him around in the next field until he was pestered by a swarm of children, all crying out for a turn. Ottus finally came and rescued him, saying, Whoa there, boy! You better save your back. Today's a day of rest and you gonna be awful sorry tomorrow if you don't use it that away.

* * * * * * * * * * *

With the coming of the mild weather, farmers all over Wills County bolted coulters to their plows and laid off their tobacco fields in two directions. Mid-way through Delmer's first week in the country the fields were dry enough to plant. The women and children dug deep into the plant beds, careful to pull the young tobacco seedlings out whole. They laid them into baskets as gently as if they were eggs, and carried them into the fields.

Though the Drew farm was only twenty-five acres to the Lawrences' sixty, they grew the same amount of tobacco, six acres of it—the maximum one family could manage. Ottus grew his in three enclosed fields behind his dark fire barn. Delmer preferred this to Ernest's one long six acre patch, which seemed endless as you started up each row. But at the north end, where the long field stopped and the weeds began, the land sloped down to where the creek cut a bow shape inside a fringe of trees and vines. Beyond the creek was the bottomland where Ernest planted his hay and corn.

The creek had been Delmer's favorite place to play when he was little, before his father died and his mother moved to town. You could enter it from under the bridge near the January place and walk inside its cool corridor of trees all the way around to the Lawrences. Further than that if you ever had time.

Delmer remembered jumping from one orange gravel bar to the next, or wading in the pooled water where arrows of light pointed down to the lazy crawfish traffic below. One time he'd found something like a crawfish etched across a rock in a gravel bar. But he had put it in the pocket with the hole and lost it.

The thought of the cool, shady creek helped him now as he followed Ola down the long rows. Carrying a basket of seedlings, she would drop one onto the mounded earth every three feet or so. He came behind with a tobacco poke and planted them, pushing their roots down into the cool dirt. Sometimes he and Ola would switch jobs for awhile to give his back a rest, but mostly he worked the poke.

The poke Delmer had been given was an old one, worn smooth with years of use. His father had whittled it from a curved ash stick so it was slightly reminiscent of a pistol, and fit his hand more comfortably than a straight peg.

He relished this connection with his dead father, who had grown steadily fainter and harder for Delmer to recall as the years passed. Now only a few images remained: his silence at one end of the dinner table; the way he sat leaning slightly forward on the wagon bench, as if he, and not the mule, provided the momentum; the swift, efficient motion of his arm as he reached for the razor strap when he needed to spank one of them; his dark eyes doing the smiling for his tobacco-chewing mouth as he waited out some long Third Monday yarn.

Ottus had given Delmer a plug of tobacco to chew, to help keep his mouth from drying out as he worked. When he had to spit out the juice it made him feel like a man. At first the rich smell of turned earth mingled with the taste of the dark tobacco juice. These were joined in his head by the ecstatic droning of flies over mule droppings, and the cool metallic smell of the creek at the end of the long field. But as the days wore on, Delmer felt heat and backache above all other sensations. In the evenings he walked through the serpentine shadows the apple tree threw across the ground beside Ottus's house and collapsed onto the front steps until supper was ready. At night he dropped into bed beside Harry, like a stone merely bearing the image of a boy.

※　※　※　※　※　※　※　※　※　※　※

Ola was worried about Ernest. He hadn't been himself for weeks, not since the McDermott raid. Of course he was overworked right now. They all were. But the pressures of work never had weighed on him like this before. This year, what with the Night Riding and all, there was a heaviness in the air and it was obvious to Ola that it was all getting to him.

Ernest? she asked him one night when they were in bed.

Hmm?

Was you one of 'em that give thirty-eight dollars to Sammy Smythe?

There was silence for a moment, but she knew full well he wasn't asleep.

Look, Ola. You and me ain't never had secrets between us that I know of, and I hate to start now. He heaved a sigh. But I'm askin you not to ask me about all of that stuff.

Ola felt something in her go sour, like the note Ernest's fiddle would fling aside when a string broke. She rolled over in bed to face away from him, determined not to cry.

After awhile, he put a hand against her back, between her shoulder blades. Just that. Eventually they both fell asleep.

She didn't refer to it again, but she read the papers whenever she had a chance and kept up as best she could with what was happening in town. Though she tried hard not to let any change come in her manner with Ernest because of his refusal to answer her question, it seemed to her that something had changed. His mood darkened day by day. For the first time the planting gave him no pleasure. He went about his work doggedly and didn't talk much.

Ola was too busy to dwell on it. Thursday, June 23rd was Lora's twenty-first birthday, and Ola was sewing her a nightgown in her spare moments, which were scarce as hen's teeth at this time of year. Ola and Ottus had agreed to make this Saturday's singalong into Lora's birthday celebration. It was the Lawrence's turn to have it and Bethy was coming, though no one else in the family could make it. Since everyone had been too tired to get together for the singalong the last two Saturdays, Ottus had talked Delmer into staying an extra day for the party.

Then on Thursday, James January and Rudy came by the house right at suppertime with the news that Ray Tibbs had been jailed. As Ola added two more plates to the table, Ernest pulled a couple of extra chairs out to the dogtrot. They took turns telling the story.

It's all over the papers, Rudy said. That goddamn Wingate jailed him for contempt of court for…

He jailed him cause he told the truth. All he done was say the judge couldn't be impartial when his own brother owns a tobacco warehouse.

Damn straight, said Rudy. Please pass the buttermilk.

Start at the beginnin, Rudy, said Ernest. What exactly did Ray say in court?

Alright, alright, Rudy bridled. That's what I'm tryin to do, if I can git a word in edgeways.

Ola glanced at Ernest, anxious that they start supper and possibly improve Rudy's mood. Ernest, will you ask the blessin?

For what we are about to receive may the Lord make us truly thankful. Go ahead.

Fred giggled. Ola gave him a look as she handed Rudy a bowl of lima beans. The two guests started eating and talking with their mouths full.

Judge Wingate asked him after he done swore on the Bible if he'd paid that bribery money to Sammy Smythe.

Wait—tell him about Wingate's threat first, said James.

Aw hell, why don't *you* tell the goddamn story since you the one knows how it ought to be done? Rudy snapped.

If any of y'all swears one more time in front of these children, I'll...

Alright, Ola, alright, said Rudy. For *Pete's sake*—how's that? Can we say for Pete's...

Suddenly Ernest stood up and banged his fist on the table, rattling the dishes and making Ralph and Ethelyn suck in their breath and then tune up. Look, you two come down to the stable with me. Y'all go ahead and eat your dinner.

Trembling with anger, Ola was left to try and calm the children down while the dinner got cold—the dinner she'd made with the last of the energy left to her after the day's fieldwork. She felt like crying herself.

※　※　※　※　※　※　※　※　※　※

After they'd finished eating, she heard Rudy and James ride away without a word of goodbye for her, and a moment later Ernest came back and sat down at the table. He helped himself to a cold supper while she started the dishes. Fred had gone off to run around the yard, and Ethelyn and Ralph were under the table playing pattycake. As soon as their father sat down Ethelyn started a game of peek-a-boo around his legs, which he tolerated without comment.

I can warm that up for you if you want me to, Ola said, in as pleasant a tone as she could muster.

It's fine. Look Ola, I'm sorry about all that stuff with them.

You cain't help how Rudy and James behaves, Ernest.

He continued to eat, as Ethelyn's *BOO* and Ralph's chortles punctuated the silence. When he finished up, Ernest disentangled his legs from their game and took his dishes over to Ola. That tasted real good, even cold.

She looked up and met his eyes, her own softening slightly. You gonna tell me what they said?

Well, it ain't good. He scraped Rudy and James's leavings into the slop jar. Wingate opened up the court term last Monday with a bunch of his blather about how nothing short of the Second Coming was gonna stop him from prosecuting the chute burners this time around. They started with all the little cases that was on the docket. Then they done the bribery investigation. They fined Ed Franklin, and laid charges against Sammy Smythe, who wasn't there, of course. Then today they called Ray Tibbs up to the stand and asked him did he pay out that money to Smythe to bribe Franklin to take care of the chute burnin charges. Ray said that yes, he done it.

Ola opened her mouth in surprise, but Ernest continued. He had already talked about it to the newspapers. He... he told us at the last meetin, that what with some of em giving checks and all, it was too easy to prove for him to go denying it. So when he admitted it in court Ed Franklin blew up, saying he hadn't never asked for nor received no money, and when Wingate told him to hold his horses, that he'd git a chance to defend hisself later, why Ray suggested Franklin jist tie his horses up at the hitch-racks in the normal way. Ever'body busted out laughing then, cept Wingate, who warned him to watch his mouth or be jailed for contempt.

So when Ray tried to explain why he'd gone along with Smythe's bribery scheme—cause goin to jail for a farmer means ruin, and how they didn't have no hope of justice in his courtroom and all—Wingate went crazy pounding with his gavel and ordered Ray hauled off. But they said Ray got off one last shout before they shoved him through the door. He said, 'Your own BROTHER owns a tobacco warehouse, Judge Wingate. You cain't pretend to be impartial on all this!' Then they flung him in jail and they put a fine of *two hundred dollars* on him, so he cain't git out for a long time. Maybe not for years, depending what happens Monday.

Ola turned away from her dishpan and leaned against the wall of the dogtrot. After a moment, she said, That's bad alright. As the silence deepened, and Ola sensed Ernest's growing depression, she sought to keep him talking. Who's gonna look after Ray's crops?

His brothers. The rest of us'll pitch in when we can.

And Maudie'll run the store of course.

He nodded. But without Ray the rest of us ain't much good. It ain't that we don't understand what the fight's all about—though God knows there's some that don't; they jist like the excitement. But *we* cain't put it to words like he does, to make a case to the people in town. Listen here to this, he said, reaching for the newspaper James had left on his chair. Listen to what Ray says here:

This bribery scheme is just one more in history's long string of cases of those in power preying on the powerless and desperate. If they lock us in jail our families will starve. So they offer us freedom if we give them money. 'Your money or your life.' It's an old, old story. What choice did we have? The action against the chute last year was a protest against a system which allows the middle men to grow richer, while those who do all the work of growing the crop remain in chronic poverty. The very people who run the court system run the chute and warehouses as well, and they seek to punish any efforts to balance the power. The punishment they are threatening us with will break us. Is this the justice the founding fathers wanted for Americans, or is it exactly what they so courageously broke away from with the War of Independence?

Ernest shook his head. Wingate knows we don't stand a chance on Monday with Ray in jail. That's what he's counting on I expect.

Ray'll have to be there, Monday, won't he? He's one of the ones indicted.

Yeah, but they won't call him to the stand, and if he says even one word they'll haul him out for contempt of court again. Meanwhile he cain't instruct Asa or nobody else on what's the best way to handle it.

You going in on Monday?

For a moment Ernest stood still, then sighed and shook his head. I've thought on it. If I thought it'd help…. Aw, ain't no use of me going in there. I'd be better off working Ray's crops for him—or working my own. I ain't no good against them lawyers and such. Besides, I ain't one of em that's on trial, so they wouldn't be inviting me to speak anyway. He pulled out a cigarette and lit it.

I got to go do the milkin, Ola said.

Jist as well. I done said too much already about all of this.

Ola felt a rush of anger return at these last words and her face reddened as she looked at him. Git the children on down to bed, she said, and set off across the yard.

✻ ✻ ✻ ✻ ✻ ✻ ✻ ✻ ✻ ✻ ✻

The next day was no better. Ernest seemed more depressed than ever, and Ola decided it was because he was being forced to bottle everything up. That went against Ernest's nature. As they went through the day she threw off her own resentment and tried everything she could think of to cheer him up and get him talking. But he just shrugged her off and immersed himself in the fieldwork. All that day he worked down in the bottom planting corn.

Ola finished up Lora's nightgown and baked her cake. The last time she had been into town for groceries, she'd included a can of pineapple rings with her order. Pineapple upside-down cake was Lora's favorite. Ola pulled it out of the oven while she was fixing supper, and left it on the back of the stove with a cloth over it. Though the tangy-sweet scent of it lingered in the kitchen Ernest didn't comment when he came in, as she thought he might.

At supper he was as quiet as a gathering storm. She'd fixed bacon and green beans and potatoes all cooked together, with cornbread on the side. It was one of his favorites, but he didn't even take any notice. What with the stove going all afternoon it was hot inside, so they ate in the dogtrot again. The children ran off to play in the yard as soon as they were finished.

Y'all keep a eye on Ralph! Yonder he comes after you, Ola called. Ethelyn turned back, dropped to all fours and crawled wildly towards the baby, making him giggle with delight.

I got to go to a meetin tonight, Ernest said, lighting a cigarette. There was no expression at all in his voice.

Ola sat looking at him, waiting for more, but he remained silent and wouldn't catch her eye. Is that the trouble? she asked quietly.

With a deep sigh he exhaled a cloud of smoke, staring out towards the calf pen where Fred was climbing the gate. They sat on in silence.

Still probing tenderly for the wound, she said, Do you have to go?

Ever'body's supposed to be there, he answered grimly.

Who's gonna run it?

Asa.

What's it for?

To figure out what we gotta do next.

She could tell he was uncomfortable talking about it. Discussing it with his wife, against orders. Feeling with each question that he might suddenly get up and leave, she reached across the table and put her hand over his. What *can* y'all do, only go to court come Monday and defend what you done?

You think I oughta go on Monday?

No. I jist mean y'all as a group. What else is there to do now?

I don't know. He shook his head, his voice a raw whisper. Ain't no telling what they'll come up with.

There was another period of silence, broken only by the evening birdsong, the laughter and shouts of the children, and the chickens' usual grumbling. Ernest finished his cigarette, flicked the butt into the yard and turned toward her, elbows on the table, forehead resting against the tips of his fingers.

Ola, he said finally, his voice heavy. I don't like the way things is going with that bunch. The McDermott business set a ugly tone. Some of em's behaving like cornered rats. And that racket of Sammy Smythe's didn't help none. The truth is... He heaved a sigh. The truth is, I'm sorry I ever got mixed up in it. Ottus was right. As he spoke the last three words, he looked up and met her eye at last.

Ola digested this confession for a moment, then said suddenly and with spirit, Well then, git unmixed. Jist don't go tonight. This ain't no real army, they cain't *make* you go. Ever man's gotta be free to follow his own mind, or what's the good of any of it?

What about standing together? he asked with a wry, regretful smile. What about 'United we stand, divided we fall'?

I ain't talking about backing down from the chute burning, or going back on the reasons you got into the Association in the first place. You still believe in them don't you?

He nodded, frowning.

Well then, I'm talking about running off the McDermotts from their farm and such as that. What's this meeting for did you say? To figure out what to do next? You already know what to do next. You go to court if you're called to and, you tell the truth like Ray done. You *got* to do that much, but you *ain't* got to go to no meeting. This here's a free country. What're they gonna do if you don't go, shoot you? She kicked at his leg under the table. Huh? Huh? What do you say, Ernest Lawrence? You gonna go to some old meeting or you gonna stay here with me?

She kept it up until he smiled in spite of himself. In the end he walked around the table and pulled her up from the chair and into his arms.

I love you, Ola Lawrence. That's what I say.

* * * * * * * * * * *

That night, as Ernest and Ola spent a quiet evening together, the Night Riders met at the Carter Schoolhouse. They filled the benches and desks, and more stood around the walls. Asa sat at the teacher's desk and asked for silence. When they couldn't hear him, he reached for the bell in front of him and rang it long and hard.

That's better, he said. Hell, maybe I oughta be teaching school. The men laughed derisively, and Rudy Oakley made a three-syllable word out of shit.

Let's git down to bidness, boys. As you know, we're in some serious manure here. Come Monday old Wingate and the whole bunch of em's fixing to nail our hides to the jailhouse door. They already got Ray in there. Now the question is, what're we gonna do?

Bust open the jail! cried a large man prized into a small desk in the front row.

Above the unintelligible tangle of suggestions that followed, rose a voice near the stove. We could lie, like they done at Dr. Amoss's trile.

Naw we cain't, said Linton Weaver. They done had witnesses namin names. They'd jist add perjury to our charges.

But them witnesses is long gone now, shouted a voice from the back, laced with the music of mockery.

I'm for visiting the judge like we done the McDermotts, Ronnie Doyle suggested.

We could do it, Cluster agreed, jist the way we burnt the chute. Jist ride in and take over the town and call him out.

Here judgie, judgie, judgie, someone sang out to enthusiastic laughter.

But Asa said, No Cluster, it ain't the same thing. Takin over a empty buildin is one thing. But takin over a house full of people right in the middle of town—hell it'd jist be war. But don't worry, I aim to leave a little message in Wingate's mailbox for Monday morning.

I say you wrap it up with a couple matches, Lubie Anderson suggested.

And a bullet, Willie added.

There was a general noise of approval at this, and more laughter.

Scarin em's the way to go, said James January from where he stood to one side of Asa. Hell, I'd wrap them witnesses up and stuff *them* into Wingate's mailbox if they's still around here. He stepped forward and spat into the trashcan beside the teacher's desk.

Ever'body knows them witnesses ain't never comin back, Rex Arthur declared. So how they gonna prosecute us anyway?

They must've found somebody else to witness against us, said Horace McDade, removing his pipe to accommodate a coughing fit.

Alright. Lemme ask you this, Asa said in the uncomfortable silence the last remark engendered. I got the membership list here, and I'm gonna call your names, cause I want a answer from ever one of you. Have *you* ever been asked to be a witness in this thing?

Now the uneasiness became palpable. Several of the men had been approached. Though they had all refused, no one wanted to draw the fire of the group to himself by admitting that the authorities had even considered he might betray the Night Riders. Willie Oakley was one such, and he began to swing his left foot unconsciously and run a hand through his hair.

Jist answer yes or no, said Asa, and he began the roll call. Lubie Anderson?

Hail no.

Joe Andover?

No!

Rex Arthur?

Newp.

Each time Asa called out a name he looked up to find the man. Arthur was in shadow. Step out where I can see you, Rex.

After that, each man stood or stepped forward to answer. The tension in the room built with each successive no. Everyone knew the authorities had been trying to find witnesses from among them, as well as in the general population. Who was lying?

When Asa called out Ernest Lawrence's name there was no response.

Ernest Lawrence, he repeated. Everyone grew still. Then men began murmuring and looking around. Rudy looked over at Willie, frowning a question. Willie gave a barely perceptible shrug.

Any of y'all know where Ernest is at? asked Asa tersely. No one spoke up. Listen, boys. This ain't no time to be deserting the Association. A absence at this particular meetin is mighty tellin, wouldn't y'all say?

No one answered, but the tone of the gathering darkened.

Maybe they done got to him, said Ronnie, and after a moment others began voicing their suspicions to those beside them. Some recalled how Ernest had denounced the McDermott raid. Others, how at first he had resisted paying his share of the money to Smythe, arguing against the whole bribery plan.

Hold on. Okay now hold on, Asa ordered as the talking swelled. If only Ray was there, he thought, then said aloud, Maybe Lawrence ain't the only one. Let's git on with the list, then we'll decide what action to take.

But when the roll call was completed with a quick no following every name, Ernest was exposed as the only one who hadn't shown up.

So, what do we do now? asked Ronnie.

Intimidation's the only thing a witness understands, said Anderson, a burly man from a farm near the McDermotts.

That's right, said another, who had enjoyed the McDermott raid. You git to this here stage, the hick'ry stick's gotta do your talkin.

What do you got to say about this, Rudy? Asa asked.

Rudy and Willie had been expecting to be singled out, being Ernest's brothers-in-law. Now that the moment came Rudy looked around the room coldly. Hell... I think he could use takin down a peg or two.

Asa drew a deep breath and nodded. Willie?

Sure, said Willie, and spat on the floor.

The Oakley brothers refrained from so much a glancing at each other for the rest of the meeting.

Alright then, said Asa. Let's plan us a visit.

Chapter Thirteen

DELMER WAS SUPPOSED TO COME BACK TO TOWN on Saturday the 25th, but when I run over there to see if he was back yet, Aunt Ruth told me he'd agreed to stay one more day on account of the party they's havin that night.

They done called over to Berry's and left word for me she said.

I was disappointed, and Aunt Ruth didn't look all that pleased herself. She was rollin out pie dough on the kitchen table. Pearl and Debry and Fairy'd gone over to Granny's for a visit.

Poor little ol youngun, she said, talking about Delmer. I know he was countin on comin back as soon as he could. But Berry said Ottus told him they hadn't had em a singalong since he'd went out there, what with the plantin and all, and Ottus wanted to thank him for his help and not have him remember it as all work and no fun. She smiled, more to herself than to me. Sides, a good dose of the country couldn't hardly do him no harm. You ought to go out there with him next time, Pat, and see what you're a-missin livin here in town where you cain't even see a storm comin at you across the fields.

I was havin my own private thoughts about what I's missin, but there wasn't no stoppin Aunt Ruth once she got started on that subject. Jist then the 4:06 from Paducah blew into town two blocks over. It was the one they called Whiskey Dick cause Paducah was in a wet county—meanin you could buy liquor there—where Wills was dry.

There. You see what I mean? Aunt Ruth went on. Here in town we're so blame bunched up against one another that storms and trains and no tellin what all can come up on you without no warning at all. She paused from workin that poor pie dough to spit into her coffee can. Then she rolled the dough up into a ball, put it into her beige-colored crock bowl and covered it over with a piece of cheese-cloth, and she give it to me sayin, Take that down cellar for me, hon, and set it on the shelf where I got my corn relish and apple jelly, will you? I wanted to have it ready for tomorrow, cause I promised Delmer I'd bake him a apple pie the day he come back home. Now then, that's a satisfaction, havin that dough done.

I took and carried the dough out the back and around to the cellar like she said, but the wind was wild that day, and it was all I could do to keep from droppin it while I was tryin to open up them cellar doors. In the end I jist opened up one of em, and had to set the bowl down on the ground, which she wouldn't of liked if she'd've saw me do it, but I had to fight that door open with both of my hands. Then I was sure it was gonna bang shut while I's down there, which would've scared me half to death. But it didn't.

I set the crock on the shelf where she said, and I'd'a stayed down there awhile if I'd a had me a light, cause the air was so cool and nice and that dirt floor felt good under my feet. But it was too spookish what with them shadders wellin and that door ready to slam shut on me, so I headed on back up to that hot wind right quick.

* * * * * * * * * *

I had went back by home to git me a drink of water fore headin off to find Hollis or somebody, when Mama caught me. She was on her way to confession and she said I needed to go, too.

Aw Mama, I ain't done nothing wrong, I said.

Right there's a lie for you to confess, she snapped, quick as could be. Mama had her own brand of psychology and there wasn't no arguin with her. Leastways not for me.

So me and Mama and Bridget Ruth walked on over to St. Joseph's Church, their skirts and Bridget Ruth's long hair jist a-flappin in the wind. They was havin a awful time tryin to walk and hold onto their hats and all. The church wasn't but around the corner up on Broadway and it was jist as well that we didn't have too far to walk.

We had Father O'Sullivan back then. He was a tall, thin Irishman and he knowed ever one of us too well for you to pretend he wouldn't guess who you was behind that little old screen. But he wasn't a yellin type of a priest. He was real soft-spoken and kind-like, so you didn't have to worry too much. I did wonder sometimes how he could be normal with us at all when he knowed ever'body's darkest sins. Still there he'd be after church on a Sunday shakin all the grown-ups' hands. And he was as natural as could be gittin up a baseball game with us boys. It beat me how he done it, but I couldn't help thinkin what high drama it'd be for him if, some Saturday afternoon, a voice from behind the screen told him it'd committed *murder*. Maybe that was what made a person want to become a priest in the first place.

Like Aunt Ruth's cellar, the church felt cool and nice. It smelt of wood and polish as we took our places in the back pew. I was jist takin notice of who was there: Miz Wingate, the banker's wife—she was nearly always there—and Mr. Lenihan, the tailor, with two of his girls that lived near Hunter, and a whole slew of Goatleys… when all of a sudden Mama caught me by the ear and yanked my head around to face the altar. She glared down at me so, I didn't need her to explain. I also knowed I had another sin to add to my list, I jist had to figure out what it was called. That's what the time before confession was for and I reckon I needed it.

Miz Wingate was takin a coon's age in there, so I run through all the sins I could remember Father O'Sullivan listin out for us in catechism class. There was lying—well, yeah—and murder, and impure thoughts, and anger, and blasphemy, and stealin, and disobeyin, and givin up on the Lord, and pride, and… holy cow, but I's gittin' the starch taken outa me jist listin all of them sins. It'd been easy a month since my last confession and I could see, now I come to it, that Mama had been right about me needin to go. It was funny how you could jist be livin your life, thinkin you's doin the best you could as you went along, but then when you went over it in your mind you'd find you'd committed a fair few sins since the last time. Surprisin what a examination of conscience'll turn up. I was wonderin whether maybe it wasn't really my fault since they always said we's *born* sinners, when

Miz Wingate finally come out and we scooched down one in the pew. Then I thought I better git to workin on my statement, cause didn't nobody else take as long as her and it'd be my turn before I's ready if I didn't watch out.

After we all finished up and said our penances and come outside I asked could I go lookin for Hollis. Mama told me I better be home by six o'clock or she'd know the reason why, but she let me go on. Then Bridget Ruth said she wanted to go down to the court square and see what was playin at the Dixie Theater, so we walked along together in that buffetin wind that never did let up all that day.

There wasn't hardly no wagons in town for a Saturday, but Bridget Ruth said it was always slower in the week after a Third Monday, and so many people'd be comin back in for the court on this coming Monday…. Well, all of that made sense.

We went around the drug store corner and Bridget Ruth slowed down. She was wantin to look inside and see who was at the soda fountain. For a minute I stood waitin for her. I looked across the street and seen the branches of Tom Tinker's tree jist a-wavin and a-thrashin as if his ghost was flyin around amongst em. Then, tired of waitin, I walked on down the block to the Dixie and seen that they had em a Rudolph Valentino picture playing. Bridget Ruth caught up to me a minute later and started on about how she jist *had* to see it before it left town. Then her friend Emily come along and I left the two of them moonin over the posters by the ticket booth.

I was headin on down 7th Street when here Hunter come, a-cloppin along on his pony. Hey, Pat! he called out. Is Delmer back yet?

I told him he wouldn't be back til tomorrow, and he offered to let me climb up behind him. Dixie wasn't very high, but neither was I, so he rode her on over to the water trough, which she liked, and soon's we could git her turned around sideways I clumb up onto her from there. The ice wagon went by goin towards Broadway just after I got mounted, and Dixie seemed to want to foller the ice wagon horse, but Hunter headed her on around the square past all the stores.

I was feeling pretty good and wavin to folks as they got their hair cut, or as they come out of Carter's Hardware with some nails or ever what it was in them little sacks they's carrying. They was the usual pairs of old men playin checkers around the square and spittin their tobacco juice onto the sidewalk. Uncle Dave was there, and so was Blackbird, a-wavin his copper bracelets and tellin a bunch of little colored boys how them bracelets was his protection against lightnin. We could smell the coffee brewin at the Black Cat Cafe, and the fry grease that wafted out of Waller's Restaurant on the other side of the square. We seen a drummer carryin his grips into the Hall Hotel, and jist as we went around a second time, the matinee let out at the Dixie, and folks—women mostly—begun a-pourin out of there. They was all in raptures over Rudolph Valentino.

Now we got mixed in with cars and buggies and people jay-walkin to beat the band. It was fun. I felt like I was in a parade, where if I'd've jist been walkin like usual I'd've missed out on it somehow. That wind was partin my hair, but it didn't seem to bother old Dixie; she jist clopped right on into it, rockin me and Hunter back and forth as we moved along.

Where you wanna go? Hunter called back over his shoulder.

I don't know, I said. Then it come to me. Hey, can we ride around past the jail?

Sure! he sung out in his enthusiastic fashion. So he headed us on down 7th Street, past the Piggly Wiggly, and right on down the next block til we was in front of the big, two storey red brick house that was our jail in them days. Miz Lemon and three of the little Lemons was settin out the front taking the breeze, jist like they had em a regular house like anybody else—no criminals in the bedrooms and no gallows in the backyard. We waved and they waved back and called, Howdy. Nice day.

Then we rounded the corner at Water Street and passed the prisoners' entrance. I was hopin to git a better look over the fence from up on Dixie's back, and I *could* see a little more of the scaffoldin of the gallows, but not a awful lot more than you could see anyway from the slight grade Water Street had up towards the Woolen Mills.

I was so busy tryin to see them gallows that I didn't notice til after I asked Hunter to turn Dixie around and stop for a minute, that the prisoners could see *us* right out of them big old barred windows. When I looked up I seen men in ever one of em, white ones in some windows and colored ones in others. It kindly gimme the creeps, but they waved to us, so of course we waved back.

We's ready to ride out of their viewpoint when Hunter gimme a
nudge in the ribs and tried to point with his head without bein too
obvious about it. Then I seen what he meant. In the upstairs window
on the Water Street end of the buildin was a man walkin back an forth
in front of his window, like a lion I seen once at the circus that never
stopped pacin his little cage. It was Ray Tibbs.

Chapter Fourteen

ON SATURDAY, JUNE 25TH, 1921, a warm south wind swept across the tobacco fields of Wills County. Twelve-year-old Delmer stood on the top step of his brother's house, watching the little puff clouds scud along smartly. He felt so light he imagined he could almost hitch a ride on one of them. They'd stopped hoeing in the middle of the afternoon and now he was free. As soon as church was over tomorrow he'd be going home.

Home. It seemed like a year since he'd seen it. He pictured their house on the shady corner of North and 14th Streets, with its long backyard full of chickens, and the stable down at the end where April stood chewing and staring mildly out at the odd wagon or car that passed. He thought of having a game of shinny or baseball in the middle of the street. Standing aside when there was any traffic and not even waiting for the dust to settle down again. The thought of their least pastimes had taken on fresh delight for him. Sometimes he and Pat would stand on opposite sides of the street as a car was coming and pantomime that they were holding the two ends of a rope. Then, just before the car came up level, they'd pretend to haul the rope taut, and the driver would stand on the brakes, honking and hollering at them.

Delmer let his mind wander back to his mother's kitchen, and the smells of ham and biscuits, or apple pie. *Oh Crikey!* he cried suddenly out loud. I's about to forgit to pick them green apples for her. But just as he rose to go toward the apple tree, Harry came banging out the door, with Ottus right behind carrying the seine. Come on, Delmer! shouted Harry. We're going fishing! Delmer made a mental note to get the apples for his mother as soon as they got back, and the three of them set off for the pond where Ernest and Fred were waiting for them.

* * * * * * * * * * *

What a mercy I baked Lora's cake yesterday, Ola thought. When Ernest and them got back she could use the stove top to fry up their catch with some potatoes and onions. It was just too hot today for the oven.

She had everything just about ready and was reaching up for the can of cornmeal to coat the fish and green tomatoes in, when Ethelyn ran through the open kitchen door sobbing. Bethy was right behind her carrying Ralph.

Sugar pie, what is it? asked Ola, squatting down to gather the heaving little body against her. Aw, there now. What's-a-matter?

I... fell... offa the... s-swing! wailed Ethelyn, and Bethy added quickly, I tried to hug her, but she jist wanted you.

Alright, Ola soothed, rocking her daughter back and forth. Okay, Allie Ethelyn, now you've got me. Come on, shug, that's enough.

Ralph watched the scene from inside eight-year-old Bethy's sliding clutch, and wasn't sure whether he oughtn't to be crying himself. He started to tune up just as his sister settled down a bit.

Tell you what, said Ola, standing Ethelyn down and wiping her face with the dishrag. Lora and Adell and the baby'll be here soon. Let's git out the box of colored glass for y'all to play with and I'll put Ralph down for his nap. How's that sound?

At the mention of the glass the girls cheered up instantly. This was a favorite pastime. Whenever a dish or bottle got broken, Ola sanded the sharp edges of the biggest pieces and added them to the box. The children loved making patterns with them out in the grass, or simply holding them up to the light to behold the world all in blue or green or amber. Today Ethelyn and Bethy carried the box to the front corner of the yard and imagined they were making a fancy window for the church, like some of the town churches had.

They were just starting to arrange them over the grass when they saw Lora walking along the road behind the baby carriage. Two-year-old Adell held shyly to a fold of her mother's skirt. When she caught sight of her cousins, she began dancing as she walked, still holding to the skirt as if it were a maypole ribbon. Lora pushed open the wide gate beneath the white oak tree, and Adell ran over to Ethelyn and Bethy, joyously calling out their names.

Ola had seen Lora coming as she laid Ralph into his crib beside the front window, and could tell by the frisky way her sister walked that she was ready for a party. Now she hurried out to greet them while Lora parked the baby carriage to the right of the front steps where the afternoon shade was beginning to grow. She looked down into the carriage. Madine was a beautiful, round baby. At three months she still radiated the full, mellow scent of newborns. Ola was tempted to pick her up, but Madine gave a shuddering yawn in her sleep and seemed utterly content in the nest of the carriage.

What do you need me to do? asked Lora. Got my milkin and all done early so I could help you out with supper.

Well, I appreciate the thought, but it's all about done for now. Happy Birthday, youngun! Ola gave her sister a hug.

Cain't call me no youngun now, said Lora with relish. I'm twenty-one and legal! Reckon I'm a woman now if ever I'm gonna be.

They sat down on the top step. As if havin three children don't already qualify you, Ola commented, raising her eyebrows.

Yeah well, not ever'body waits til they's old and grey to marry, Lora teased.

Old and grey! Why I was twenty-three is all.

Exactly. And Ernest near thirty! Law, now that's pushin it, you gotta admit.

As they bantered on in this vein they saw a wagon approaching from the east. To their surprise it was Rudy. He pulled up at the gate, hopped down, opened it and led the mule on through before they could help him.

I done come for Bethy, he announced shortly, heading towards where the girls sat in the grass with the colored glass.

But I thought she's gittin to stay for supper, said Ola, walking out towards him.

Rudy called to his daughter to come on home. Ignoring the child's protests, he pulled her roughly by the arm, lifted her up onto the wagon, then climbed up after her.

Rudy? Ola tried again.

I best git her on home, he said, without meeting his sister's eye or explaining the sudden change of plan. The girls called and waved to Bethy as the wagon rolled away in a building cloud of dust that blew across them all. Lora and Ola gave each other an eloquent glance, set their jaws and let it pass.

Watch the children for me while I go do my milkin, will you Lora? Ola asked, already walking towards the stable. Lora nodded and reached down for Madine, who had begun to cry.

         ❅ ❅ ❅ ❅ ❅ ❅ ❅ ❅ ❅ ❅ ❅

While waiting with Fred beside the pond, Ernest's mood had taken another downturn. He was anxious to know what had happened at last night's meeting, and had half expected Willie or Rudy, or maybe James January, to drop by today and ask him where he'd been. It seemed odd that no one had. By rights he should've gone by one of their places and asked about it, but he wasn't yet ready to explain himself. He would have to eventually, he knew that. He even understood that the longer he left it, the harder it was likely to be. Still he hesitated, sinking deeper into inner conflict as the hours passed. He'd see them at church tomorrow; that'd be soon enough.

Ernest knew as well as anyone how seriously they all took being in the Night Riders. He also knew it was getting out of hand. The McDermott raid had been a sorry business. The Night Riders were supposed to be against the tobacconists, not against other farmers. It was one thing to visit people about joining the Association; it was another to run people off just because you didn't care for them. The stealing should've been handled by the court. Jackasses though they were about the chute burning business, thought Ernest, the lawyers and judges were capable of handling a straightforward case of stealing, particularly when thieves left the stolen goods right there on their property for anybody to find.

Ernest's brown study was interrupted by a long whistle from Delmer. When Fred saw the others coming over the rise in the meadow, he jumped down from the persimmon tree he'd been climbing in and ran to greet them. He and Harry laid the seine beside the pond and began unrolling it from either side.

Why Ernest, I expected to find a pile of fish in that washtub once I got over here, Ottus remarked with a smile. From back yonder it looked like you was hoggin, you's settin there so still.

I wouldn't even attempt it with a expert like you around, Ottus.

Do it, Daddy! cried Harry, pausing above the seine. Soon all three boys were clamoring. Yeah, come on Ottus. Hog us a big un. Jist one?

Aw, y'all'd never keep still long enough for me to catch one that away.

Ernest stood quietly, his smile preoccupied. But the others persisted until finally Ottus waded slowly into the reeds and sat back on the bank of the pond. He hunched forward, dangling his fingers loosely in the water, letting them hang down like fronds which moved only with the water's own motion. The others gathered behind him to wait, keeping perfectly quiet.

Y'all git over to my left, so I won't hit you in the face with him, whispered Ottus, and they complied, Fred and Harry giggling at the image.

They settled in to wait as long as necessary. Perhaps five minutes passed. Just when Fred thought he couldn't stand it a moment longer with the mosquitoes tormenting him, a big bass swam into view a few feet away. Harry caught his breath and almost called out, but Delmer clapped a hand over the younger boy's mouth. Everyone tensed into a frieze against the blue sky, except for Ottus, who seemed to remain utterly relaxed and still, as if dreaming. Though the wind whipped a lock of hair over his forehead, he never moved, concentrated completely upon the fish that swam closer and closer.

The bass turned slowly among the reeds, curving this way and that, enjoying the cool shade that the still bulk of the group on the bank cast across the edge of the pond. Finally it swam beneath Ottus's long fingers and hung there, allowing the almost imperceptible motion of those fingers along its sides.

Ottus awaited his moment, barely tickling the fish behind its gills. Then the moment came. The fish breathed, and Ottus grabbed it by the open gills, lifted and flung it back over his right shoulder in one violent motion. The long-held tension of the group behind him broke in a four-voiced cheer. Even Ernest's mood was lifted by Ottus's prowess.

As Ottus stepped up onto the bank, his pant-legs streaming pond water, Ernest grabbed his right hand and raised it like a prize fighter's. Presenting the all time hoggin champeen of Wills County!

Behind them, as if in anticipation of Ola's frying pan, the fish flopped desperately in the endless green flamescape of the meadow.

❊ ❊ ❊ ❊ ❊ ❊ ❊ ❊ ❊ ❊ ❊

After seining the pond and sorting the big fish into the washtub, they threw all the small fish back in and rerolled the net. As the group walked back across the fields to the house, Delmer suddenly asked, We goin straight over to Ernest and Ola's?

Sure are, answered Ottus. That's where we're havin the fish fry. Lora's gonna meet us over there.

Well I jist gotta run over to your house first. I promised Ma I'd pick her some of them June apples to bring home.

Why do you have to git 'em now, Delmer? asked Ottus. Why not in the mornin?

Tween church and packin up and all, I'm afraid I'll forgit. I'd almost forgot anyways. I won't be long. Delmer was already running south as the others bore northwest.

Okay, Ottus hollered after him, but it looks to me like you're jist tryin to git out of cleanin these here fish, little brother!

Delmer turned around, running backwards for a moment, to gauge whether Ottus was serious and really getting mad at him. Seeing that he was only teasing, Delmer grinned and waved and turned back around.

Nice kid, said Ernest.

He cain't wait to git home, that's certain.

Yeah, Ernest replied without any energy.

They were carrying the washtub of fish between them, following behind their small sons, who struggled to share the burden of the dripping, furled net. They walked on in silence for awhile. Finally Ottus spoke up.

Ernest, what's eatin you these days? You ain't yourself.

Well hell, Ottus... Ernest began painfully, surprised to be asked. Monday's that chute burning trial, and... well things ain't looking so good.

Ottus was sorry he'd asked, because there wasn't a word he could say that wouldn't sound either condescending or confrontational. Look, if it comes to you goin to jail, I'll help Ola out all I can—you know that.

Ernest felt an ache pass through him, like the slow notes Hardin could draw on his bass fiddle. Here was naked proof of the character of Ottus's friendship—the way he leaned, not on their differences, as he might've, but on what bound them. Ernest didn't know how to go about explaining his worries, which weren't about being jailed himself. He looked down into the tub of dying fish. Finally, believing it would be improper to go into the business of the missed meeting and the Night Riders, he said simply, I do know that, Ottus.

They walked on in a slightly lighter silence, Ernest determining to shake off his brooding, no matter what it took. Beyond their boys, the old house stood surrounded by waving trees. Built fifty years before, it had been home to two large families prior to Ernest and Ola's. Now it held their wives and children, who were preparing for a party.

As they approached the gate, Ottus directed the boys to unroll the seine and drape it over the fence to dry. They did so, then each one scampered off to tell his mother about the fine silver catch in the tub. Ernest smiled at the way Ola and Lora both whooped and carried on for the sake of their firstborn sons. Then Delmer came running up, his pockets full of green apples, and the party began.

*   *   *   *   *   *   *   *   *   *   *

They ate supper out in the dogtrot, where the breeze was like another guest at the table, welcome even though it meant a little more trouble. Afterwards Ola refused to let Lora help clear the dishes. She put a firm hand on her sister's shoulder as she started to rise, saying, Now you stay put, honey. I think, since Harry and Fred caught the fish, *Adell and Ethelyn* oughta help clear up.

Adell, remembering her mother's birthday surprise, jumped up right away with an officious air. Ethelyn had been about to suggest they go back to their colored glass game, but her frown quickly changed to a smile when she caught on.

Madine began to fuss on Ottus's lap and he handed her over to Lora to be fed. She accepted the little bundle in the yellow receiving blanket, crooning, Aw, come here, precious. Come to Mama. She knows what you need.

Ernest rose to get his fiddle from the front room, remembering as he did so to take Ola's shotgun down from its pegs and carry it inside for the night. He placed it under his rifle above the mantel and collected the violin from where it hung, further along the wall. Just as he returned, Ola emerged from the kitchen with the cake. The girls walked ceremoniously ahead of her, each carrying a present for Lora.

Since she was nursing the baby, Lora muted her enthusiasm to an awed whisper. She reached out with her free arm and put it around Adell, holding her close as she leaned over to kiss Ethelyn. Aw, y'all shouldn't have. Why looky there, it's my favorite—pineapple upside-down cake. Ola, you sweetheart!

As she beamed around at them all, Delmer hung back embarrassed. Ottus leaned over and kissed her lightly on the mouth, making Fred and Harry wrinkle their noses and turn away in disgust.

Well, looks like I cain't open these presents myself, so I reckon you girls'll have to open em up for me. The girls tore into them with such delight that Lora added, Jist remember — I git to have what's inside.

Ola had made her a nightgown of cotton, printed with lilac sprigs. Ethelyn cooed over it and held it up as if she hadn't watched her mother working on it all week long.

I don't know why you're thankin her, said Ernest, getting into the spirit a little. It was Delmer and me *made* it. Everybody, including Delmer, laughed at the image of the two of them sewing the pretty nightgown.

Adell finally got her tiny box open. Inside, on a cushion of cotton, was a locket engraved with two interlocking hearts.

Aw, Ottus. I'm gonna cry here in a minute.

The children shouted for her to open the locket. With Madine in the crook of her arm, still happily nuzzling away, Lora prized the little hearts apart. Ottus had put in a picture of himself in his wedding suit, and one of Lora at about sixteen, just as she had looked when he'd asked her to marry him.

Lora looked over at Ottus, and Fred, sensing another tender moment, pleaded, Don't kiss her again!

After coffee and cake, the adults began to sing, starting with Lora's favorite, Swing Low, Sweet Chariot. Delmer took Fred and Harry out into the driveway for a top-spinning lesson, while Ralph lolled sleepily on Ola's lap. Ethelyn and Adell went back to the fence corner to play with the glass.

The sun declined under a pink doily of clouds, and a full moon rose, but the singing went on and on. One or another of them would leave to visit the outhouse, or to put a child to bed, but the music never stopped. Delmer sat up with the adults, unwilling to admit that he felt increasingly drowsy as the softness of dusk crisped into hard-edged night.

It had been decided that when the party broke up he was to push Madine in the baby carriage, while Lora and Ottus carried the other two home. For now they lay Harry and Adell in Ernest and Ola's bed against the back wall, with Madine in the carriage beside them.

That ought to keep Adell from falling out, Lora whispered to Ola as she snugged the baby buggy alongside the bed. She's the wildest sleeper you ever did see.

Jist like you was then, Ola replied with a fond smile, as they went back out to the dogtrot.

The south wind that had blown all day long was blowing still and felt good in the warmth of late June, even as midnight drew near. Cotton-headed with sleepiness, Delmer tried to listen as the adults became embroiled in a discussion about Dixie.

I don't care what anybody says, Ola was saying. The Civil War changed ever'thing, includin Dixie. It cain't be sung jaunty-like no more, the way it was wrote. It's a lament now. Ought to be done slow—like you played My Old Kentucky Home for me that time, Ernest, member?

Ernest leaned back in his chair, his eyes half-closed. Mm-hmm, he mumbled affirmatively.

Well I think you're plumb crazy, said Lora. Ain't nobody plays Dixie that away. Suddenly Ernest sat up and pricked his ears.

What's the matter? Ottus asked.

After a moment, Ernest said, Nothin I guess. I thought I heard a horse whinny down by the creek, but it must've carried down from the barn on this wind.

Well, I'm bout ready to head on home, Lora said through a yawn. Y'all, this was the best birthday party of my whole life. I couldn't never thank you enough.

They gathered up the coffee cups and pie plates and took them inside. Then they went to fetch the children. Ottus set a coal oil lamp on the table beside the door. All eleven were there and Lora was tucking her presents into Madine's buggy, when a bullet shattered the upper pane of the window over Ralph's crib, showering him with broken glass.

Ola screamed and ran to get the baby, but several more shots were fired over their heads and suddenly all the women and children were screaming.

Ernest moved instinctively towards the guns over the mantel, understanding with instant and sickening certainty what he had suppressed when he'd heard the horse down by the creek a few moments before. Midnight. A shot through an upper pane. Night Riders.

When the initial screams subsided, they heard several of the men outside laugh, perhaps at the little chorus that had resulted from their shots. Ottus was standing up against the wall beside the door trying to see how many there were, but he couldn't see much from inside the lamplit room.

Lora had picked up Madine and gathered her three children beneath her on the back bed, as hens gather chicks under their wings when a storm rises. Ola had managed to get Ralph, but was having difficulty gathering the others. Ethelyn had run to her to hide in her skirts and was hampering Ola's attempts to get to a rear corner of the room, away from the door and window. She backed over her little daughter, knocking her to the floor. Fred was sitting up in his bed in the front corner, his face blanched with terror and confusion in the light of the lamp.

Suddenly Asa Miller shouted, Ernest Lawrence! Git on out here!

Ottus turned to Ernest with a questioning frown. They were after *Ernest* and not him?

But Ernest never saw Ottus's unasked question. He stood staring at the door for an instant, then reached up for his rifle.

No, Ernest! Ola pleaded.

Ernest! Ottus hissed. Throw me the shotgun.

Come on out here, Ernest! Asa shouted again. We wanna talk to you. And your wife, too!

Suddenly the trance Ernest was in broke. Rage lit him like a torch and he reached for Ola's gun, shouting, Ain't nobody touchin my wife! He threw the shotgun to Ottus.

Oh yeah, we touchin your wife alright, sneered a voice Ernest didn't recognize.

As soon as he caught the gun, Ottus slid down into a squatting position and trained it on the front steps. Git down, all of you, he whispered. Blow out that lamp!

Delmer dropped to all fours and crawled across to Ottus, hiding himself behind the door. He drew his knees up into the circle of his arms in an effort to clench his violent trembling.

Ola sank to the floor, pulling Ethelyn and Ralph to her. Fred slid out of bed and crawled towards his mother. For an instant they slipped free of time; the scene froze like a photograph. Ernest was almost paralyzed again with surging emotion, staring blindly at the gun in his hands, pierced by what he had brought on them all. Then Ottus cocked his gun beside the open door. Asa's horse skittered sideways and gunfire erupted from both sides.

Shots rang through the room from two directions as Ottus fired out at the men in the yard. With the answering gunfire, the shots from outside picked up and were no longer aimed high at the door and window. Suddenly Ottus slumped forward, blood seeping out from under him, his body pinning the door against Delmer. Though Delmer sensed the shifted weight, he was too frightened to look up or move from where he had hidden himself. He lay his head on his knees, trying to mute his sobs.

Lora looked up and saw, then lay back over her children, saying through tearing sobs, It's... o... kay... it's... o... kay...

When Ernest saw Ottus fall he cried out, Oh my God, no! Through the broken window he could see men with torches riding around and around the house now. Though he couldn't make out who they were, he fired into them wildly. Then a bullet caught him in the head and Ola saw him fall backwards in front of the fireplace. The shooting thinned out almost immediately, and she heard a man cry from outside, Both men's dead! For a few minutes there was only the sound of horses circling the house. Then even that slowed and the only sounds were stamping, neighing and the jingling of harnesses. The children began to whimper and cry again.

Suddenly there were footsteps on the porch. Her crying children clinging to her, Ola made her way to the axe on the wall beside the door. Git Daddy's gun! she ordered Fred, who stumbled towards his fallen father in the dark. Fred was shot in the back as he ran, and fell face down in the middle of the room.

Before Ola could even scream, Lubie Anderson filled the doorway, with several others behind him. He laughed when he saw Ola, a baby in one arm, raising the axe at him. There had been no plan to kill any of them, but the answering fire had changed things. As soon as Ottus had been killed, most of the men understood there was no going back. Lubie Anderson had a taste for violence and hadn't hesitated to lead the charge into the house.

Grinning at Ola he threw his pistol to the ground and stepped over Ottus's body. Ola raised the axe to strike him with it, but he wrenched it easily from her grip. She put up her hand to shield herself and Ralph as the man sliced downwards. Her severed hand fell to the floor. The axe had shaved off the top of her left shoulder, and Anderson raised it again and brought it down on the mother and her screaming child. Even after they fell, he slashed again and again in his bloodlust, until the axe lodged in the floor.

Rex Arthur had come through the door behind Anderson, James January behind him. January had been in the thick of the crowd and hadn't been able to resist following Anderson and Arthur inside. Now he stood in the doorway over Ottus Drew's corpse, looking by torchlight upon the room he'd known so well as a neighbor. January had seen farmhouses full of dead bodies during the war, but this was home, and these vanquished enemies that lay strewn and bleeding, these were the Drews and Lawrences.

He could still hear babies crying as he grabbed the coal oil can from under a table and began sloshing oil around the room. At the same time, Rex Arthur saw Ethelyn crawling away from her mother's skirts, and raised his gun and shot her in the head. Then, turning to where Lora looked up from the back bed at the sound he shot her as well. Each shot made January's arm jerk spasmodically as he poured the oil. He meant to be neat and only anoint the floor, but the shots caused him to splash the furniture and bodies. Out of all proportion to reason, this bothered him.

Goddamn it, Lube, Arthur called to Anderson, who was still leaning over Ola and Ralph's bodies trying to work the axe out of the floor. Let's git out of here!

January threw the oil can to the floor beside Ottus's body and the three of them fled the house, just as Asa lit the wall on fire. He tossed the hickory stick he had planned to use on Ernest Lawrence, in through the door. Someone threw a torch into the house and a swift conflagration lit the way for some fifty men on horseback, who rode out through the open gate and split up in several directions.

✻ ✻ ✻ ✻ ✻ ✻ ✻ ✻ ✻ ✻ ✻

Willie and Rudy Oakley had kept to the rear of the mob, not daring to move as the violence escalated. Now they rode away towards their own farms, Willie swearing savagely. They passed Linton Weaver, who had stopped to throw up over the side of his horse. Both understood for certain Ernest and Ottus had been killed. Ronnie Doyle had confirmed that much. It wasn't til James and the others had come out of the house empty-handed that they realized nobody was going to escape. That was when Willie turned a demented face on Rudy and said, You ever let on to a soul we was here, I swear I'll kill you.

Rudy's mouth was so dry he couldn't utter a word, but he lit out like a jockey at the first opportunity. He rode home and put his lathered horse into the barn without a rubdown, stumbling into bed to lie in an agony of dread beside his sleeping wife.

James January rode to his place, his heart pounding, his breath coming in short gusts. After dismounting he stood awhile in the stable doorway, staring at the fire that haloed the hill. Finally he came to a decision and ran into the house to tell his mother that the Lawrence place was on fire. I'm goin into town to tell their people.

Well… mercy, James, said Mrs. January in an effort to clear the sleep from her head. Is they anybody hurt? Shouldn't you oughta go over there first, to see can you help?

He hesitated, then answered, I done been over there already. The fire's too far gone to fight, and ain't nobody home over't the Drews neither. I aim to tell their folks in Greenberry.

She gasped. I heard em. I heard em all a-singin earlier. You don't suppose… the whole bunch of em's…. Before she could finish the question he had already gone back outside to remount his tired horse.

January rode through the silent countryside like one possessed. The full moon cast his shadow large and sharp to one side, but his mind was too busy to notice such details. He must keep his story simple, he told himself. *I got up to go to the outhouse, and that's when I seen the glow of the fire. I rode over, past the silent Drew place, and seen that it was too late to fight the fire. Come back past Ottus's and knocked at the door. Nobody home. So I hurried on into town to tell their relations.*

As he rode into Greenberry, several sleepers half woke to wonder who was in such an all-fired hurry. A few lingerers at the Black Cat Cafe looked out the windows in the wake of the rapid hoofbeats, but saw nothing.

January went first to Ruth Drew's in Tobacco Town. He pounded on her front door until she opened it. She pulled her wrapper around her and squinted out crossly. Fairy, Debry and Pearl came up behind her, rubbing their eyes and asking who it was. Seven-year-old Fairy pushed her way up beside her mother and held onto Ruth's wrapper.

Fraid I got some bad news, Miz Drew. The Lawrence place is on fire, and it seems like Ottus and all them was over there tonight. Looks like there ain't no survivors.

For a second Ruth was silent, poised on the brink of a long fall from normal life. Then she began to scream and her daughters followed suit. Ruth put her hands up to her head and called out in an elongated wail, Oh Ottus! Oh *Del*mer!

Chills pricked January's scalp. I only got my horse, he said. Who can you git to take you out there?

When her mother didn't answer, Pearl burst out, Uncle Berry. He's got a big buggy.

Y'all git dressed while I go git him then, he said.

Before going to Berry's over on West Broadway, he rode around the corner to tell Hardin and Nell, then Granny Rule. After that, beginning to enjoy his position as the compassionate bearer of bad news, January rode over to Berry Rule's.

The last stop he made was at Mrs. Hayden's Boarding House at 10th and Broadway. Throughout the following week, when January's story was in hot demand, he told this particular episode this way:

I tied my horse up to the railins of Miz Hayden's porch and went on in through her front door. But jist as I put my hand on the stair post to go on up to the Smith's, Hazel Oakley—I mean Hazel Smith—she stepped out from the shadows underneath of them stairs. Liked to scared the wits out of me. It was like she was waitin for me. And before I could say a word, she says, in that gravelly voice of hers, she says, 'All I got to say is they's burnin. They's a-burnin in hell right now. What goes over the devil's back'll come under his belly someday.'

Chapter Fifteen

WHAT WOKE ME UP WAS BERNARD, gettin into his clothes and tellin Mama and Papa, I'm comin too. A lamp was on in their bedroom, and I couldn't see much, but it was clear to me ever'body was leavin the house in the middle of the night. So I got up and drew on my overalls. When Mama seen me she got all tore up.

Aw now, Pat, you're a-stayin here. Ain't no tellin what we're liable to see out yonder.

Though I still didn't know what was goin on, I wasn't about to stay in that dark house with jist Bridget Ruth, and her a-sleepin like the dead the way she always done. Papa used to say Bridget Ruth'll sleep through the Second Coming, so I didn't reckon she'd be much company after ever'body else left, and all I knowed was that something big had done happened.

When Papa went out the front door I follered after him. Later I was wishin I had me a jacket on, but my nightshirt had long sleeves at least, and I knowed it'd heat up a right smart soon's the sun come up. Papa met Granny on the sidewalk and they hugged and cried, sayin Ain't it awful? and such as that. I walked along behind em around to Aunt Ruth's, and once I went up onto her porch and seen all of her girls a-settin there cryin and heard Papa and Granny tryin to comfort Aunt Ruth, I started to piece out what was happenin, and I felt my insides drop down like guts into a tub. Delmer *dead?* And all the rest of em too? Well I commenced to shakin like I had the palsy.

Shortly after that Mama and Bernard come, then Uncle Berry with his wagon, and him and Papa helped Ruth up onto the bench. Fairy was clingin to her so hard she had to ride up there too, and Granny. The rest of us piled into the back and didn't nobody say too much. Mama didn't even seem to notice that I had disobeyed her and come along. But then I was feelin quieter than I'd ever felt in my whole life. I don't reckon I said a word from the time I woke up til I seen Hunter later that day. But I'm gettin ahead of my story.

Uncle Berry drove that wagon as hard as I'd ever saw one drove, and we could see the glow of the fire long before we turned onto the windin road that led past the January farm and Ottus's house—which was still and dark—and on to the Lawrence place where Papa had been born and raised. It was still burnin when we got there, the open gate and that white oak tree carved out black against them roarin flames and glowin half-walls that used to be the Lawrence's house. I looked over at the others and seen the reflection of it burnin in their eyes, tears drippin orange down their cheeks.

There was a automobile parked on the road beside the gate. Three men from the Hickory Grove chapter of the Woodmen of the World, which Papa belonged to too, was standin there gawkin. They had even fetched Brother Walker when they seen the fire. Said they'd saw it when they was coming out of a meeting. Papa drew out his watch. He said later it was one-thirty in the mornin.

Brother Walker strode real fast over to the women as they started towards the gate. Oh my dears, I am so sorry, he said. Y'all mustn't go any closer. He tried to hold Aunt Ruth in his embrace and turn her around, but she was cryin louder now and strugglin against him.

Mama put her hand on the minister's arm and said, Thank you kindly, Brother Walker. We know you mean well. But this is something we gotta do.

Papa had clumb the white oak and looked down through the house where the roof had done fell in. He come back to the ground white as a sheet and shakin his head. They're all in there, he said.

So ever'body linked arms and started walkin real slow towards the fire. Aunt Ruth and her girls and Granny let out a sorta wail that stood the hair up on the back of my neck, but we all kept goin forward til we was stopped by the heat of it. The flames was near as tall as me, and the wind was at our backs, blowin em away from us. Still there was heat, and there was the smell of burnin logs and other stuff it's best not to go into.

The log walls made a sort of cradle around em, and little by little we begun to make out what we was seeing. Some turned away as soon as that happened, but I was paralyzed-like and couldn't stop myself from lookin. Though the bodies was all swole up you could still make out their clothes and such. Ernest lay on his back in front of the fireplace with a rifle acrost him. Fred was face-down in the middle of the room, not far from his daddy. They was a heap of bodies to Fred's right. Lora was spread over her three younguns on some collapsed bedding. Ottus lay near the door, with a pistol, a shotgun and a coal oil can close by him.

And now... well... the last one is the hardest for me to tell about. It was Delmer. He was settin up, so you could see ever line of him clear enough to cut through you like a knife. He was crouched behind the door close to Ottus and had his head on his knees, with his arms all wrapped around his legs. The picture ain't never left me and I don't reckon it will if I live to be a thousand.

Aunt Ruth fell to the ground a-wailin and some was tryin to comfort her, but we was mostly all in shock. Me, I stood off to one side, jist a-starin. Finally, when I felt like I could move, I turned away. The fire lit up the yard and I stumbled around in it. There was Fred's wagon, and then I noticed for the first time, Ottus's fishin seine draped over the front fence.

But the thing that got to me most of all was when I walked around to where the back steps had been. There, close to the path beside the garden, I found Delmer's red top layin in the grass. My heart give a little lurch and I plunged down and picked it up before anybody else seen it, and put it down in my pocket where I could keep my hand around it. It almost felt like I'd been able to save some part of Delmer or something—which I knowed was foolish. Still I kept my hand on it, and it give me something. I... I cain't explain it.

I don't know how long any part of this took. Time didn't act like it usually does. The moonlight cast shadders acrost them smokin ruins and I thought about Granny and Padrig, out here on jist such a night, eager to build em a weddin house according to the signs. And now here was poor Granny seein the sorrowful end of that careful-built house, and holdin up her grieving daughter for all she was worth and her near bent double with grief herself.

The light finally come up that mornin—though I wasn't so sure it was goin to—and showed us all wanderin around helpless and dazed. By then more people had begun to turn up. Family and neighbors and I don't know who all. Word was spreadin. The flames had died down, and people was millin about, askin what in God's name had happened, and ever now and then a fresh wail would peal out as somebody else come up to the scene. Then the rooster crowed—like it was jist any old mornin.

Me and Bernard was standin beside the front fence, starin at some colored glass spread out across the grass in the corner. It was all like the worst dream you ever had, and wasn't none of it makin no sense.

Suddenly Mama come up behind us. Bernard, she said, serious as I'd ever heard her, and we liked to jumped out of our skins. I don't know how much more of this I can stand. Bridget Ruth's going to be wakin up by herself soon and we're goin to have to go back to town for a little while. Granny wants you to ride out to Panther Creek and tell the folks there what's happened. Go over to Ottus's and git his bicycle. It'll likely be beside the front porch or somewheres. You ride out to the Beans and tell em. They'll give you breakfast, and then they'll want to come and see this for theirselves. We'll have to come back too, so we'll meet up with you out here later on. Pat, you go tell Hardin I need to get on back to Bridget Ruth.

I seen Papa squatted down close to the burnt house. I had reached a point where I couldn't look at them that had been burnt up like I had at first. Later on I would be able to again, but for awhile there I couldn't. Anyhow, a glance told me their bodies was shrunk down and blackened now, and the stove pipe and chimney and a baby buggy frame was about near all that stuck up out of a smoking heap of white ashes.

Papa had his head down and I thought he was cryin. The very notion set my head a-spinnin. I didn't know what to say to him. I hadn't never saw Papa cry and I knowed if he broke down I would too. So I squatted down there beside of him all worried-like and looked up into his face. But he wasn't cryin at all. He was studyin the ground. He turned real slow and looked at me like he'd jist saw a vision from the underworld, and he pointed to the ground. There I seen what I hadn't noticed before—a whole bunch of fresh-beaten horse tracks encirclin the house.

Night Riders, Papa said. It was Night Riders done it.

* * * * * * * * * *

We went back into town to get dressed proper, to pick up Bridget Ruth and to eat. Mama said we had to get some eggs in us or we wouldn't never stand the day we was in for. Well all the way we passed buggies and cars, people on horseback and in wagons. They was all goin out to the fire site to see it for theirselves. It made Papa so upset he didn't know what to do to think of all of them people pokin around and starin at the bodies and all. But there wasn't a thing we could do about it.

So we hurried up and got back out there ourselves, and it was jist like Papa said it'd be, a dadgum circus. We had to park way down the road and fight our way back in there and it wasn't but about eight o'clock in the mornin. By early afternoon, when all the churches let out, it got so bad that most of the fence around the Lawrence place was trampled flat, and there wasn't no grass left at all, just churned up mud. The only corner that crowd respected was where them pieces of glass was spread out. They left that part alone cause Bethy Oakley had done told how it was the last game them children had been playin before they was burnt up and ever'body'd spread the word about it. Rudy and Faye had come by the time we got back from town.

Of course, Sheriff Jones and his deputies was there, and the coroner... and reporters. Strange thing was, by afternoon reporters had come from newspapers as far away as Memphis and Louisville and St. Louis. By evening even New York City and Chicago had men there. They was combin the crowd and anybody that had a story to tell would get swarmed. There was photographers, people drawin pictures, and writin out notes—why this was the biggest thing ever to hit Wills County by the look of it.

Some time after we got back, Fred Ailsworth come through the crowd, led by Deputy Wyatt. He was carrying a shovel and rake over his shoulder, and sort of smilin at the crowd, proud to've been asked to be the one to remove the remains from the ashes, which was still a-smoulderin. They had give him a pair of real thick boots for the job. Miz January brought some sheets and wash-tubs. Then the Carter Hardware Company men come through with a long wicker casket and announced that they was donatin their services for free.

I stood there beside Papa, tryin not to get shoved forward by the crowd behind us that was pushin in to get a look, while Fred Ailsworth shovelled up what was left of Delmer and the Drews and Lawrences. Aunt Ruth hadn't never left the scene all day. We'd brung her back some food to eat, but she never touched a bite—not for days I reckon.

They was tryin at first to keep the two families separate, putting the Drews in one end of the long basket, and the Lawrences at the other. Aunt Ruth had pointed out Delmer to em, so Fred Ailsworth shoveled up his bones real careful-like and put em into a iron bowl beside the wicker casket. I don't know why she wanted him kept separate, but wasn't nobody gonna refuse her a thing that day. The coroner, Mr. Fenton, he picked around through Delmer's remains with a pair of tongs and brought out what he said was baked apples from a fold of cloth. That was when Aunt Ruth broke on down. Uncle Berry hadn't left all day neither... nor Granny. So all them went on back to town at that stage, leavin us to catch a ride with somebody else, which we knowed we could without no trouble, the traffic out & back bein so heavy.

Right up til the day she died Aunt Ruth would talk about Delmer wavin to her from the back of that wagon, his bare feet hangin down and him not wantin to go. The grief of it stayed fresh in her, losin em all that away, and she—and all of her girls too—had nightmares the rest of their lives. With all of her sorrow, Aunt Ruth become easy prey for ever kook that come through town sayin they could unlock the mysteries of the universe. She'd *always* cross their palms with silver and ask what happened to Ottus and Delmer and them. Who done it? And most of all, *why?* Oh, they'd tell her it was a man who died with his boots on. Or a man who escaped from town on the train wearing a dress and bonnet. Then they'd have their money and she'd be left in that same old cloud of misery.

But that day, soon after Aunt Ruth left, Miz Oakley arrived from Tennessee with her two oldest sons. They tried to support her and walk her towards the casket, but she collapsed and fainted a few feet away. Same thing with Ernest's mother, who'd come from over in Missouri.

Willie and Rudy moved through the crowd, cuttin their eyes this way and that and refusin to talk to reporters. People was givin them and Hazel the eye and whisperin behind their hands about how they had always been jealous over the land. Cause naturally the talk started runnin to speculation about what had happened exactly. How could eleven healthy people have died in a one-storey house-fire?

By the time we come back from town them guns and that axe was gone, wrapped up in a sheet and took back to the sheriff's office as evidence. Coroner Fenton had drawed him a little sketch of the house in a tobacco warehouse ledger, notin down where each body had laid, and about the weapons and all. So most of the folks millin around them ashes thought at first that it was jist a house-fire. Still it didn't add up, even without the axe and the guns.

I heard one woman guessin that they had et adulterated ice cream and then knocked over a lamp and been too sick to get out once the fire started. Another said maybe lightnin had struck the house.

Why shoot, said old Horace McDade, anybody can see this here's a murder. I saw Willie Oakley jerk around and give him a look that'd scare the devil hisself, but old Mr. McDade carried on, real loud. Ever'body knows Ernest Lawrence was kicked in the head by a mule when he was a youngun. Had spells ever since. I reckon he must of had one of them spells a his and shot em all, then turned the gun on hisself.

Well that rumor spread through the crowd right quick and in no time flat Mr. McDade had a swarm of reporters on him. But when they asked Dr. Barton what he thought of this theory, they got em a earful sure nough, and it turned up in the *NEW YORK TIMES*: I brought Ernest Lawrence into this world thirty-five years ago, and I've been his doctor ever since. If he'd had a head injury of any kind—or 'spells'—I would know about it. Whoever says he did is a liar. Ernest was as fine and stable a man as I've ever known.

That same New York reporter then asked Deputy Meshew what he thought of the murder/suicide theory. He was jist as sure about it as Dr. Barton. These families were murdered, that much is certain, he said, causin ripples of comment among the crowd around him. After the murders, the house was saturated with oil and burned to cover the evidence. It was the work of an insane person, or persons. But these people were attacked from the outside. As to who did it, I don't know. I only know this was no ordinary house-fire. It was murder.

It was after that when I begun to hear the name Oakley whispered through the crowd. Rudy's wife and children was there. And both Bethy and Faye had been talkin about what a close call it'd been for Bethy—how if her father hadn't happened to pick her up early the night before, she'd've been in the house too. And James January was a big hit with all them reporters, with his story of Hazel Oakley Smith steppin out from underneath of them stairs in the middle of the night and sayin they's all burnin, before he could even break the news to her.

When Rudy got wind that suspicion was startin to fall over him and his brother and sister he panicked. He'd been looking pretty haggard and wild anyway, as who wouldn't with so much of their family layin dead before em. But now, with the whiff of a lynchin outrage in the air, he took off like Nudie's ghost and wasn't seen for a week. Folks said later he hid out in the Viola Bottom and lived off the land til he reckoned it was safe to come out again.

I was standin there watchin Fred Ailsworth puttin his grisly harvest on them white sheets. On one sheet, was a handful of coins, and the blackened pieces of a fiddle, its strings curling upwards like question marks. Then, from underneath the skeleton of the baby carriage, he fished up a locket and chain and laid it beside the rest. After it had cooled off some, Mr. Fenton opened up the locket, but the photographs that was in it was all blackened. I was watching all of this when I heard Hunter's voice beside me.

Hey, Pat, he said kindly quiet-like.

I glanced at him and nodded, and we just stood there awhile, neither one of us knowin what to say. Like I say, I hadn't said a single word for hours and was about to forget how. It was like there was a smothering in my throat and couldn't nothin come up through it.

Gosh... I... I jist cain't believe it, Hunter said, his face workin some. I jist stood there swallerin. Finally I said, Me neither.

I know we was both feelin the need to mention Delmer, but was afraid to speak his name in case we'd start bawlin right there in public.

After awhile I decided I could take a risk and I whispered, Look. I pulled Delmer's top out of my pocket, and Hunter was hit real hard by seeing it, I could tell. He made a sort of stranglin, gulpin noise. Then we was both back to not talkin. The quickest sort of glance was all we was able to give one another, but it did us. He stood beside of me til his folks come for him.

The *DAILY LEAF* had their people out workin the crowd for donations for a monument. They had these signs printed up sayin *Give To The Monument Fund*, and people was clinkin coins down in their cans all afternoon long. Both sets of Wingates was there and lots of the high muckety-mucks, as Papa called em, pokin and pryin and smirkin behind their hands over the chickens scratchin around in the henyard and such. Oh it was a free-for-all. Ain't no tellin what Delmer would've said if he could've saw it, nor Ernest. But Ottus, he'd've hated all of them gawkers with a purple passion.

They had done carried them sad little piles of rubble they called the remains back to town in the Carter hearse, and folks was gettin so carried away with all the excitement—talkin of the horror and mystery of it all, and of our town makin the *NEW YORK TIMES*—that the general atmosphere was gettin out of kilter altogether, when somethin happened that shocked em all back to reality and finally caused the crowd to start dispersin.

It was along about four o'clock. Somebody had brung Fred Ailsworth a plate of brains and eggs and a jar of cool well water. It wasn't long after he'd handed em the empty plate and gone back to his work, that he raked a hand out of them ashes. It wasn't much more than a blackened skeleton, but it was a human hand all the same, and it caused the crowd to draw back. Some people screamed, two fainted, a few retched.

There'd been skulls and all earlier, so it's hard to explain how this one hand got to ever'body so. But it did. Somehow that hand all by itself was enough to make you sick. Enough to carry the notion of what had happened. And it didn't help none that it was wearin a weddin ring.

* * * * * * * * * * *

Since most people's wagons and cars was already full, Papa had to arrange us different rides back to town. Hunter was already gone when I found Mama and them in the crowd, and me and Bridget Ruth ended up takin a ride with Miss Rose Lenihan, the aunt of them girls that lived on 8th Street near Hunter. Miss Rose'd come out in her buggy all by herself and had to go through Greenberry to git back to her farm south of town, so she was happy to take us.

I knowed Miss Rose to see, cause she peddled milk and eggs in town real regular, and also cause she went to our church. She was a small woman, with wispy brown and grey hair that didn't wanna stay pinned in the bun she wore on the back of her head. She was a big talker, too, and full to bustin with grievous information about this 'tragedy' as she kept callin it, which I reckon was the right word.

Law, she said, waitin her turn to pull into the long line of cars and wagons that was goin back to town, if this ain't the worst thing that ever took place around here I don't know what is.

The Drews are our first cousins, said Bridget Ruth.

You don't mean to say! Oh, well of course, they would be. I hadn't put that together.

We nodded, and Miss Rose looked at us more careful-like and bit her lip. She shook her head and pity, for *us* now too, filled up them grey eyes of hers. Jist about the time I was startin to squirm on her leather buggy seat somebody called to her to go ahead, so she clicked her tongue and said, Git up, Virgil.

It was a slow ride home. Miss Rose was real nice to us, talkin away the whole time and bein careful of our feelings. I don't member much of what she said, but I can recall one part. She was talkin about how she had sometimes met Ottus at the tobacco market and she had knowed his daddy, Perry Drew, too.

You know, we—my sister Mollie and me that is—we ain't in the Pool neither. (That was what Miss Rose called the Association—the Pool.) I expect they don't push it with us much, on account of us being women—though I know it can happen that the Night Riders'll visit women too. You know, I don't know what I'd do if they was to visit Mollie and me—I jist pray it'll never happen. Ottus Drew and me, I'd say we was in agreement on it, though we never discussed it outright. But all of this unrest here lately has made me remember somethin I had forgot all about. When I was a child my mother and father had em a friend who was full-blooded Cherokee, name of Lauda Stamper. Her mother'd had to give her away to save her from havin to go on the Trail of Tears. So the Stampers took her in, and then, when it was learned her mother died on the way out to Oklahoma, they ended up raisin her. You could tell to look at her that she was a Indian, and she lived all her life scared that the government'd find out about her and make her go out there to a reservation.

Anyway, that's her, Lauda Stamper. Well, she used to stop and visit with us sometimes, and I remember one day she was lookin out over our big tobacco field when all of a sudden she said, 'My people never grew this much tobacco. They kept it for special ceremonies, and only grew what they could use in a year. Your people grow too much of it,' she said to us. 'It ain't good.'

I was still chewing over this your people my people stuff when we got to 13th Street. Mama was on the porch and invited Miss Rose to come in, but she said, Thanks, Nell, but I better get on home. My cows'll be calling for me by name if I don't hurry it up.

It made me smile despite ever'thing to think of them cows calling out *R-o-s-e,* real long an low. She said goodbye, an if there was anything she could do.... Me an Bridget Ruth thanked her for the ride. After that Miss Rose always smiled at us in church, on account of our bond.

* * * * * * * * * *

That night me and Bernard and Bridget Ruth lay in our room for hours, and couldn't a one of us git to sleep. The dark corners of the ceiling was full of stuff I wisht I had've never saw. And I didn't, oh I *didn't* wanna think about Delmer ahidin behind that door. So the three of us kept on talkin and talkin. Usually Papa would've yelled for us to hush up, but he didn't that night.

Bridget Ruth talked about how she never would get over us goin off and leavin her asleep. And we told Bernard about Lauda Stamper. And then Bernard told us about his trip to tell the relations over at Panther Creek. He said between the moon and the dawn, he didn't need no lantern when he set out for the Drews' place. Said he could see rags of dew arisin up and blowin acrost the fields, and could hear whippoorwills callin, so that by the time he got to Ottus and Lora's he was spooked sure nough.

Ottus's bicycle was leanin up against the porch like Mama said it would be, but jist as he was about to take aholt of it, he looked up at their house, and for some reason the thought struck him to go inside and look around.

The place was all dark and silent and he said he could almost hear his own heart as he started up onto the porch. Just as he put his hand on the doorknob a car come roarin up the road on its way to the fire, and he seized up for a instant til it went past. Then he went on ahead and opened the door.

He went into the front bedroom, and could feel as much as see, the furniture bulkin out from the walls—them two beds and the wardrobe that we knowed from havin been out there for the singalong, and other times. By then he was just a-shiverin, not knowin for sure there wasn't some murderer hidin out waitin for *him*. In the other bedroom was Ottus and Lora's bed and a crib. He said it was eerie. He almost expected Ottus or one of em to walk out from the shadders and ask him what he was doin there.

On his way into their little back kitchen he tripped over a alphabet block and sent it clatterin into the baseboards. But the kitchen had more light in it, what with the east window beside the cookstove. On the table was a bowl with three small June apples in it. Salt and pepper shakers. A oil lamp with two matches laid out beside it, all trimmed and ready for them to come home to in the dark.

He walked over to where Lora's apron and a assortment of jackets was hangin on pegs beside the back door. Gatherin them clothes one by one against his face, he said he could tell which was Ottus's and which was Lora's by the smells alone. Tobacco smoke, sweat, cookin and soap mingled and clung to em, and named names. Ordinary good smells, not like them comin from the burning house yonder.

Jist thinkin of them other smells made him suddenly have to pitch out the back door and vomit over the porch railin. Then it swept over him that he needed to get as far away from there as possible, as fast as he could. Dippin him up some cistern water, he rinsed out his mouth, and then went on around the house to git the bicycle.

He pedalled east and south on the back gravel roads of Wills County like the legions of Satan was after him. While he was glidin along like that, something inside of him let down and his emotions started to churn, he said. Now that he was all by hisself and doin a job, his mind commenced to revisitin the massacre, body by body. Jist past the Trace Creek Baptist Church, a farm dog come up out of the ditch at him and like to scared him to death. He said he kicked at it as hard as he could, and it went a-yelpin off into the woods.

By now it was gettin brighter and roosters was callin out their raspy warnin to ever' farmstead, that it had better be about its bidness. Bernard wiped the sweat from his forehead with his shirtsleeve and kept on ridin. It was full mornin when he turned in at the driveway of the first Bean farm. They was down in the stable milkin the cows, and he went in and told em the terrible thing that had happened.

* * * * * * * * * * *

The next mornin was a Monday, but so many people wanted to go to the funeral that the Woolen Mills closed at noon, like it was a Saturday. The sky was grey and they was prophesying rain.

We read in the *LEAF* later that they had went on ahead and held a session of court that mornin. Coroner Fenton swore him in a jury to investigate the deaths of the Drew and Lawrence families. He called up six people to testify, four neighbors (though not the Januarys), and two of them Woodmen of the World we'd saw out there when we arrived. The neighbors all said they'd heard em singin til near about midnight. Then they'd heard gunshots and screamin. Didn't a one of em go for help, and nobody in the court even asked em why not. Them Woodmen said by the time they got there it was all over, an the only person they went an got was Brother Walker. Ever'body spoke of the good characters of the victims, and said they didn't have em no enemies so far as anybody knowed.

Mr. Fenton ruled that they had '...come to their deaths through foul play, but we do not know the cause'. Judge Wingate accepted the coroner's report, continued the Night Rider cases—jist like that—and let ever'body out by noon so they could eat their dinner and still get to the funeral by two o'clock.

That was that. Them chute burning cases got continued like clockwork ever session for years, til I reckon they just quit bothering to say it. Sammy Smythe was brought back, like I said, about two years later and served a couple of years of hard labor in the Eddyville Penitentiary. But he kept on runnin for office, even from inside the Pen. Never did get in though. But I'm gettin ahead of my story.

It wasn't til later we heard about all a that stuff. That morning we didn't know nothin about what was goin on in the rest of town. We was busy tryin to get our Sunday clothes in order and such as that. I had a devil of a time gettin my feet into my shoes, like I did ever time I was made to wear em, but I didn't complain about it that day. Mama and Papa and Granny—well shoot, all of us—we was so cut up an sad we didn't hardly know what we was doin. I did remember to get Delmer's top out of my overalls and put it in the pocket of my Sunday pants. From the minute I found it, I aimed to keep it with me.

We was told they was sendin a ambulance around for Aunt Ruth and her girls to go to the funeral in. Granny had stayed with Aunt Ruth for the night, and she was to go in the ambulance, too. Uncle Berry was comin for us. Papa said Frank McClain, a friend of Ernest and Ottus, had offered to let the Drews and Lawrences be buried in his plot in Maplewood Cemetery, since neither family'd had em a plot. Naturally they was all gonna be buried together in the one grave. Delmer too.

Once we got to Maplewood, it was rainin kindly light, but all the same there was a mob a-waitin around the McClain plot. There must've been close on three thousand people, Papa reckoned. Ever'body I could think of was there, seemed like. Hunter and his family, and Hollis, too. The Wingates, and the Washams, and such. I never seen Miz Washam by then without wonderin if she had her little bitty gun on her. Course the mayor and sheriff and all of them come, and Dr. Barton. Father O'Sullivan was there too, and Reverend Hicks. Ray Tibbs was still in jail, but his wife Maudie had come with her girls, and Cluster Higgins, and Horace McDade. Rudy Oakley wasn't there, cause as I done said, he was hidin out in the Viola Bottom. His wife stayed away, too, far as I know. But Willie come, and Hazel and Earl Smith. They wasn't none of them lookin any too sturdy. Hazel was sorta mutterin under her breath an smoothin at her clothes, and

Willie kept takin off his hat and puttin it back on again, and looking all around him.

There was even a big group of colored folks way at the back. I recognized most of em. Fred Ailsworth was giving Uncle Dave the low-down on what was happening. Blackbird was there, and of course George Adams and his whole family, along with Klute Walker and our other neighbors on 13th Street. Moses Galbraith had come, and Noble Duffy. Papa said the rest of em had done farm work for Ottus and Ernest.

We filed right on up beside of this big hole in the ground and I looked down into it. They was a fresh smell of earth, and some rain puddled way down in the bottom so I seen a drizzly image of myself looking up out of it. I stepped back some then and studied the wall of the grave. They was shiny shovel marks on it, and little sprigs of roots stickin out here and there.

We was surprised when the preacher from the First Christian Church in Greenberry got up and stood at the head of the grave like he was going to conduct the service. All of them that had died was Methodist, and, except for Delmer, Brother Walker was their minister. We looked around for him, and there he was, jist standin in the crowd near Willie. Turns out some of the townsfolk who figured the eulogy would make the big city papers had got involved, and they'd insisted that Dr. Wooler would make a tonier speech than Brother Walker. Also First Christian had a big old choir in white robes to do the singing. This made Mama so mad she forgot to be sad for awhile, which maybe was a good thing, but to this day I still think Brother Walker should've preached the funeral. Anyway I knowed what the deceased woulda had to say about it.

We stood there waitin in the soft rain while people collected more money for the monument they was wantin to raise up. Reporters took pictures, their powder flashin silver off of all them wet, black umbrellas. Then the cream-colored Carter hearse turned into the cemetery follered by three other black cars. Miz Oakley and Miz Lawrence each had them a hearse too, looked like. Papa said later it was the first time any of em had rode in a automobile, not that they was in any shape to even know how they'd got there.

Them vehicles parted the crowd and brought a hush over anybody that was still whisperin. First the coffin was took out and set into a sort of brass frame that was around the open hole. The dirt they had took out of there was in a big old mound to one side, with three shovels stuck in it, ready to go when the service was over. They had switched them remains out of that wicker casket they was usin before and put em into a fine wooden coffin with three brass handles on either side. And there was some flowers, two different bunches, laid along the top.

Soon as that was set up, they brung out the three mothers. Papa and Uncle Berry come forward, and them undertakers handed Aunt Ruth and Granny over to em. Pearl an Debry an little Fairy follered behind, Fairy cryin when she got separated from her mama for a minute. Aunt Ruth looked for all the world like Mary in the thirteenth station over at church—the one where Jesus is taken down from the cross. Her long, thin face was so pale and twisted up I didn't hardly recognize her. Granny stood right beside of her, jist like she'd been ever since we got the news, and Fairy wouldn't let go of her skirt. Their eyes looked like two holes burnt in a blanket, like they say.

Once ever'body was in place, Dr. Wooler begun to speak. ELEVEN PERSONS IN A SINGLE COFFIN! he bellered, and those of us who was standing up close almost sunk to our knees at first from the volume, let alone what he was saying. I reckon he was shoutin to be heard over the rain and out to the edges of what Papa said later was prob'ly the biggest audience he'd ever had. But, shout he did, the veins jist a-standin out on his neck.

My brothers and sisters, this is indeed a sad day for Greenberry. Let us bow our heads, and listen to the words of sacred scripture: *The day of the Lord will come like a thief, and on that day the heavens will vanish with a roar!*

Here the preacher cast his eyes up to the low ceiling of grey clouds over us. Ever'thing he done was real flourishy, like the side-show men at the county fair ever' August. He looked from the sky down into the grave for a minute, then he went on.

The elements will be destroyed by fire, and the earth—and all its deeds—will be made manifest. Two Peter, Verse Ten. My good people, this is a warning that is repeated throughout the Bible. Time and time again we are warned: We know not the hour nor the day. I am coming like a thief in the night, therefore STAY AWAKE!

Now these poor eleven victims lie before us like the perfect em-
bodiment of the word of God. And what a noble fate—dear, bereaved
ones—what a noble fate, to illustrate the sacred word of God!

But we the living, how are we to stay awake all the time, one might
justifiably ask. Had these poor, unfortunate people been awake, they
would not have been consumed by fire...

I looked up at Papa. He had his eyes shut and was shaking his head
in a tight little motion, like it was all he could do to keep his mouth
shut and listen. A quick glance, and I seen I wasn't the only one
lookin around right then. Plenty of folks was cuttin their eyes back
and forth, though most stayed fixed on Dr. Wooler.

We all know it is impossible to stay awake every minute. We are
only human, and weak like the disciples in the Garden of Gethsemane.
Then what does God mean when he *asks* us to stay awake? How can
one stay awake always? I will tell you how! Not in the body, but in the
soul can a man stay perpetually awake. For it is not the body God is
concerned with. It is not the body He warns us about. The body is
nothing, as we see only too well. Here he swept his arm over the coffin
in front of him, kindly pitiful and dismissive-like.

The soul, on the other hand, is everything. The life of the body
is too uncertain to contain our hopes and dreams. Why, thirty-eight
short hours ago, these eleven souls were walkin around just as you
and I are this minute, in their eleven bodies. Now they are one, in this
coffin, and—we earnestly pray—one with God in heaven.

We are all members of one body, brothers and sisters. All this great
crowd together could be reduced to ashes and fit into a single coffin
if the fire be hot enough. If we are Christians that is our hope and our
salvation—to be one in Christ Jesus. Let us stand together then, and
join the choir with one voice!

The choir of the First Christian Church moved forward in their
white robes and begun to sing Nearer My God to Thee. Little by little,
more and more of the crowd joined in, their voices blendin above the
soft sound of the rain that jist kept on a-fallin.

I'd been holding onto Delmer's top the whole time. All of a sudden,
while they was all a-singin and the preacher's eyes was closed, I
stepped forward and dropped that red top down into the grave between the brass rail and the coffin. It was done fore I had a chance to

think about it, jist a impulse that had took aholt of me. I stepped back right quick and looked around, part of me wishin I hadn't'a done it. I had thought to keep Delmer's top forever—that winner of contests, that breaker of teeth. I don't know to this day what possessed me. Maybe it was Delmer hisself, wantin it back.

But it was done, nothin I could do about it now. When I looked up Mama caught my eye, an I knowed she'd saw me do it. She was lookin at me with real sad eyes. I thought sure I was gonna catch it, but you know what? She never did smack me or even scold me for it. Ever.

Epilogue:
June 25, 1996

IT'S A PERFECT SUMMER AFTERNOON. Eleven people sit in a circle of lawn chairs placed carefully in the middle of a pasture, a couple of miles northwest of Hickory, Kentucky. There were supposed to have been fifteen people present, but by a strange coincidence, eleven have come. This is sacred ground. The north end of the pasture slopes down to rich bottomland in which huge golden bales of hay lay this way and that, waiting to be collected. The bottom is skirted by a tree-fringed creek. In a meadow nearby, several cows have waded into a pond, and stand gazing out over the tobacco fields beyond.

Each person in the circle holds a slip of paper with a name written on it. One of them, an eighty-six year old man known for his large gestures and animated stories, sits quietly studying his piece of paper. On it is written the name of a schoolfriend lost to him seventy-five years ago to the day. Delmer Drew. The best top-spinner and marble shooter at West Ward School in 1921, murmurs Hunter.

Beside him sits Pat Rule, eighty-four, and wearing a sad smile as he looks around him and remembers the house that stood on this exact spot when he was a boy. I don't understand it, he says. The road used to come along through that field there, past the Lawrences and on past the Drews. It's completely gone, no sign it was ever there. He is holding the name of his first cousin, Ottus Drew. Various friends and family members have come together to remember and honor the Drews and Lawrences on this seventy-fifth anniversary of their deaths. Because they loved music, and were singing almost up to the moment they were killed, *these* eleven sing. Songs of grief and solace float up from the circle: Amazing Grace, Abide With Me, Softly and Tenderly, Dona Nobis Pachem.

After the singing, a few spontaneous prayers are voiced, and the story is told again of what happened here June 25, 1921. Then, one by one, each reads out what is written on the paper he or she is holding, and the others answer, *Present.*

> Ernest Lawrence, thirty-five years old
> Ola Lawrence, twenty-eight
> Fred Lawrence, almost five
> Ethelyn Lawrence, almost four
> Ralph Lawrence, eleven months
> Ottus Drew, twenty-four years old
> Lora Drew, twenty-one
> Harry Drew, almost four
> Adell Drew, two and a half
> Madine Drew, three months
> Delmer Drew, twelve years old

After a moment of silence, people begin talking about what they remember or have heard of the lives and deaths of the Drews and Lawrences. But the sun is relentless, and eventually drives the little congregation of eleven into the trees at the edge of the pasture, where they sit telling stories and wishing to keep the circle for awhile longer. Finally, after one last prayer and many hugs, they get into their cars and drive slowly back over the tufted fields, where the road no longer goes.

Dark Fire Timeline

Jan. 29, 1920   Crisis in local tobacco market; wagons held up.

Mar. 23, 1920   Association meets in Paducah; mass meeting announced for Mar. 26 in Greenberry with Felix Ewing as guest speaker.

Mar. 25, 1920   Night Riders burn the chute in Greenberry.

Mar. 26, 1920   Ewing addresses mass meeting of the Association; warehouse owners place armed guards at their homes and businesses.

Apr. 1, 1920   Night Riders send out warning notes to individuals.

Apr. 2, 1920   Governor orders troops into Greenberry to restore order.

Apr. 12, 1920   38 men indicted with arson; witnesses protected.

June, 1920   Night Rider cases continued in court for lack of witnesses.

Nov., 1920   Night Rider cases continued in court for lack of witnesses.

Jan., 1921   15 separate 'visits' made by Night Riders in Fleming and Bath counties; Governor offers reward for arrest and conviction of 'terrorists'.

April, 1921	Night Rider cases continued in court for lack of witnesses.
May 30, 1921	Night Riders in Wills County beat the McDermott family and run them out; they flee to Oklahoma.
June 16, 1921	Sammy Smythe attacked by Ed Franklin in court square for spreading rumors that Franklin accepted bribes from Night Riders to oil their cases through court.
June 17, 1921	Night Rider cases scheduled for June 20th.
June 20–24, '21	Newspapers and court full of Sammy Smythe; Night Rider cases moved to June 27th, but not continued.
June 25–26, '21	Drew/Lawrence massacre.
June 27, 1921	Fragments of eleven bodies buried at Maplewood; Night Rider cases continued indefinitely.

Notes & Acknowledgements

ANY CREATIVE NONFICTION BOOK 'takes a village', as they say. This one took a county and more, involving what feels like a cast of thousands both in the research and in the story itself. All the stories in *Dark Fire* are true, told using the tools of fiction. I take responsibility for any mistakes, but must give credit where it's due. I am deeply grateful to those who shared their opinions and memories—many of then first person accounts, since I did my research more than 25 years ago. Indeed, that research began when, as a child, I listened to stories told by the adults in my life, particularly my father, Louis Bernard "Yardstick" Rule, and my paternal grandmother, Nell Touhey Rule. My mother, Elizabeth Lenihan Rule, added her perspective, as did my brothers and sisters, cousins and other relatives.

I owe a particular debt to my sister Bridget for her expertise with photography and other forms of visual art, my sister Angela & nephew Brian for sending the family photographs they had, my brother Michael for his genealogical research, my cousin Sandra Simmons and her mother Fairy Drew Simmons, for their stories and photographs. I am grateful to my cousin Darlene Easterwood for helping me spread the word about the book in Western Kentucky. Thanks to my cousin Jason Rule, who searched his family photographs for images from the period. My Aunt Frances Sholar Rule taught me about soap-making and how laundry was done in the 1920s. I have framed much of the story from the point of view of my uncle, Pat Rule, and will be forever grateful to him for his invaluable stories, as well as his wit and his knowledge of this period of history. I only hope I've done justice to his unforgettable voice. Indeed I owe more than I can ever repay to all of my family, my siblings Rosemary and Tim, my children Justin, Ross and Carys, and everyone not yet named here, for their unflagging support, not only in sharing their perspectives and talents, but also in reading the many drafts of *Dark Fire* and giving honest and generous feedback. Without them this book would not have been written.

So many friends have contributed to my understanding of the story that I could never name them all, but I must list some of them. Lon Carter Barton, the historian of my home county, provided not only his own stories, but keys to open the door to many people and places which would have been closed or unknown to me without his beneficent patronage. Driving around the back roads of the county with Lon was both hilarious and educational. I will never forget his friendship. Dr. Hunter Hancock, a close friend of Delmer Drew, told colorful tales of their games & exploits. He and Pat are the architects of my sense of Delmer's character. Jeannie Neihoff Spraggs explained much to me about tobacco farming and hog killing. But even more importantly, she took me into the bosom of her wonderful family when I was young, giving this town girl a window on growing up in a large, warm Kentucky farm family. Ernie Nelson introduced me to people who were alive in the 1920s and who had great stories to tell about it. He and his entire family embody generosity in a way that is extremely rare. To me, the Nelsons have always been an extended branch of our family. Dr. Charles & Dr. Lillian Daughaday shared their understanding of the Night Rider era with me and have always been encouraging. Fireman Ian Grey explained to me how fire consumes bodies, though it caused him pain to do so. Wesley Bates, John and Mary Terpstra, Alvaro Tortora, Jeffery Donaldson, Graeme MacQueen, and Will Rueter read early drafts of the manuscript and provided insightful comments which improved it enormously. They, along with other friends in the Hamilton writing community (and outside the writing community, for that matter!), as well as everyone at Bryan Prince Bookseller believed in this book and encouraged me through the long years of its journey to publication. I cherish you all.

I'm also indebted to Canadian writer Sandra Birdsell, and to two well-known Kentucky writers who read all or part of the book and provided encouragement: Wendell Berry and Bobbie Ann Mason. Heartfelt thanks, particularly, to John Terpstra and Bobbie Ann Mason for their generous gifts of time and their eloquent and positive comments for the back cover. And I'm extremely lucky in having found Greg Smith of Blind Pig Press to design the book, and to help me in so many ways. Thanks to Greg, and to Bruce Simpson for steering me to him.

Over the years, I took careful note of the people I spoke to in Mayfield and Graves County (called Greenberry and Wills County in the book), but it's possible I've left someone out. If you helped me, and don't see your name here, thank you, and please forgive the omission. Time and death only strengthen gratitude. I am deeply grateful to the following, many of whom are now deceased:

Martha Babb

Mrs. Beatrice Bruce

Dr. Thomas D. Clark

Judge Bill Cunningham

Sylvia Doores

The Filson Club

The Graves County
 Courthouse

Laura Hall, of the University
of Kentucky Periodicals Dept.

Georgia Ruth Jackson

The Kentucky Dept. for
 Libraries & Archives,
 specifically Bill Richardson

H.C. Lawrence

Mary Frances Drew Morris

Orma Boyd

Aubrey Byrd

Will Ed Clark

John L. Davis

Mrs. Lura Mae Emerson

George Coon Library
 Princeton, Ky.

The Graves County Public
 Library

Caspar Hopkins

Tommy Jones, of the Pottsville
 Cemetery

Jeff Lamb, of Maplewood
Cemetery

Prentha Lawrence Maritt

Gladys Morse

Notes &Acknowledgements

Sandra Murray
Lucille Powell
J. Logan Pryor
Earl Richardson
The Secretary of State's
  Office, specifically Jamie
  Sanderson
Wayne "Twister" Turner
Helen Lawrence Webb
William Wells
Jenny Hopkins Wilson
Sam & Betty Workman
The Wrather Museum

The Pogue Library,
  Murray State University
Ruby & Ray Reed
Mark Riley
Mrs. Lenore Shaw (nee Smith)
Mrs. Marie Sullivan
Tobacco Town Museum
Klute Walker
Elizabeth Wells (nee Lockridge)
The West Kentucky Dark Fire
  Tobacco Growers' Association,
  Murray, Ky.
Rick Yates

Obviously, *Dark Fire* was a complicated and painful story to write. I want to go on record as being in support of unions, though not in any way condoning the violence depicted in this book. As a teacher, I was a proud member of a union, and saw firsthand that workers must stand together to ensure that those in power fulfill their duties justly. What happened to the Drew and Lawrence families was reprehensible in the extreme, and only highlights the need for sound and intelligent leadership, which was critical then, and is no less critical today.

Finally, I want to explain that, while the stories in *Dark Fire* are based on true events, I have fictionalized the names of some, but not all of the characters and places. Since my goal was to re-member the Drews and Lawrences, I kept their names, and those of my own family. I invented names for many others, including the Night Riders, the Oakleys, the judge and his brother, and the various officials and ministers mentioned. Some of the people I interviewed asked that I not include their names in my acknowl-edgements. I have honored these requests, but the fact that they were made illuminates my motivation in telling this difficult story: to help unlock the fear that can silence justice. Heartfelt thanks to all who have helped me to bring this story of the Drew/Lawrence massacre to the page. My hope is that, in some way, it gives the victims back their lives.

Further Reading:

Allen, Hall, *Center of Conflict: A Factual Story of the War Between the States in Western Kentucky and Tennessee*, published by *The Paducah Sun-Democrat*, Paducah, Ky., 1961

Craig, Berry, *The Hidden History of Western Kentucky*, The History Press, Charleston, South Carolina, 2011

Clark, Thomas D. *A History of Kentucky*, The John Bradford Press, Lexington, Ky. 1960

Cunningham, Bill, *On Bended Knees: The True Story of the Night Rider Tobacco War in Kentucky and Tennessee*, McClanahan Publishing House, Kuttawa, Ky., 1983

Davis, D. Trabue, *Story of Mayfield Through a Century*, Billings Printing Company, Inc., Paducah, Ky., 1923

Gardner, R. H., *Those Years: Recollections of a Baltimore Newspaperman*, Galileo Press, Aiken, SC, 1990

The Graves County Genealogical Society, *Graves County Kentucky: History & Families*, compiled and edited by the Graves County Family History Book Committee: Nancy Courtney, Mary Nell Dowdy, Beverly Gourley, Anna Houser, Diane McGee, and Mildred Wheeler. Turner Publishing Company, Paducah, Ky., 2001

Hall, Suzanne Marshall, *Breaking Trust: The Black Patch Tobacco Culture of Kentucky & Tennessee, 1900-1940*, dissertation, Emory University, Atlanta, Ga., 1989

Kleber, John E., Editor in Chief, *The Kentucky Encyclopedia*, The University Press of Kentucky, Lexington, Ky., 1992

Levin, Elizabeth, *The Reign of the Nightriders*, Christopher Publishing House, Boston, Mass., 1932

Miller, John G., *The Black Patch War*, University of North Carolina Press, Chapel Hill, NC, 1936

Ogilvie, Frances, *Green Bondage*, Farrar & Rinehart, New York, NY, 1931

Vanderwood, Paul J., *Night Riders of Reelfoot Lake*, Memphis State University Press, Memphis, Tenn., 1969

Warren, Robert Penn, *Night Rider*, J.S. Sanders & Co., Nashville, Tenn., 1939

Waters, John C., his unpublished papers, given to the Pogue Library at Murray State University upon his death in 1967

Werner, Carl, *A Textbook on Tobacco*, Tobacco Leaf Publishing Company, New York, NY, 1909

Werner, Carl A., *Tobaccoland: A Book About Tobacco, its History, Legends, Literature, Cultivation, Social & Hygienic Influences, Commercial Development, Industrial Processes & Governmental Regulation*, Tobacco Leaf Publishing Company, New York, NY, 1922.